C000081273

The happynurses guide to

Creating a Balanced Life

The 12-week coaching plan for busy nurses

by Claire Westwood

RGN, RSCN, BA (Hons) Health Studies, Dip Life Coaching

The happy nurses guide to creating a balanced life – the 12 week coaching plan for busy nurses

© Claire Westwood.

ISBN: 978-1-906316-30-3.

Published in 2009 by HotHiveBooks, Evesham, UK.

www.thehothive.com

The right of Claire Westwood to be identified as the author of this work has been asserted by her in accordance with the Copyright, Designs and Patents Act 1988.

A CIP record of this book is available from The British Library.

Designed and typeset by Caroline Curran Graphic Design, Bath.

Printed in the UK by TJ International, Padstow

Contents

Introduction	Create a balanced life	2
Week		
1	**Who are *you*?** Your values, beliefs and skills. Create a map of you.	5
2	**Your current life balance** Using the Wheel of Life.	13
3	**How healthy are you?** Simple steps for more energy and greater well-being.	19
4	**Your environment** Making your home a nurturing place to be.	31
5	**Work and career – enjoy earning money!** Discover what you love in the world of employment and business. Find a better match for who you are.	36
6	**Your friends and family** Identify your friends, supporters and responsibilities.	43
7	**Communication and confidence** Improve communication with yourself and others and develop confidence.	55
8	**Money – the root of all evil, or good fun?** Make your money work for you. Gain control and learn where to find solutions to the mystery of wealth.	63
9	**Organisation and time managment** Learn to utilise your time well, find time for relaxation and pleasure.	70
10	**Challenge, fun and happiness** Find real happiness through 'flow'.	76
11	**Your inner self** Examine your personal and spiritual development.	81
12	**The 12-week plan** How to coach yourself, maintain enthusiasm and motivation.	88

www.happynurses.co.uk

Create a balanced life

- *How do you feel when you read those words? Scared, excited, terrified, puzzled?*
- *Do you know what that means for you? Do you believe it?*

I have many of the same feelings as I sit and write this book. At the moment it consists of a few lines of text on my screen, but if you are reading it, then it must now be a fully completed book! My decision to write this book was based on a desire to let others know what I know, to share my knowledge and experiences and construct an 'actionbook' to move you from where you are in life now, to where you want to be. Completing the exercises will enable you to live a healthier, happier, more amazing life.

What makes this book different from other coaching books? Well – it is written by me! No one else could write this book, as no one has had my experiences and training, or has read the same books, or has my ideas.

When you set out on *your* journey, it will be unique to *you*. No-one else can do it. How amazing is that? Imagine if some of the following people had not set their goals and achieved what they did – how different the world might be: Thomas Edison, the Wright Brothers, Bill Gates, Nelson Mandela, Oprah, Steven Spielberg, JK Rowling, Elvis Presley …

This book contains important and interesting facts, ideas and information, but there is far more knowledge available on these topics than I can cover, so I will be referencing other books and websites throughout each chapter. You can read as many, or as few, of these as you wish – read up on subjects that you find more interesting or challenging. The whole journey will be one of inspiration and discovery.

In order to tackle the areas of your life that affect your health and happiness, you should ideally set a goal of reading one chapter each week, answering the questions/exercises and completing a simple action or two. Decide now how you will find that time – when can you fit in the reading and exercises? It will be time well spent! Remember to allow for some thinking time.

After 10 weeks of working through the book, longer if you need it, you will have completed small, easy actions in various areas of your life and confronted some of your life issues. You will be feeling healthier and have a better understanding of yourself. Completing the questioning exercises will also help to move you in the right direction – knowing your values, skills and strengths is extremely valuable information.

Imagine a staircase of 12 steps – covered in beautiful carpet, or made of real oak. It looks really inviting. On the level at the top you can see a happier, fitter, more excited version of you. This will be you in 12 weeks' time!

Each step on the stairs is a chapter of the book and takes you nearer the new version of yourself. In the same way that you wouldn't try to leap up a staircase all at once (unless you are a pole vaulter!), you take it, literally, one step at a time.

One action. One a day. One week at a time. It all adds up.

You can, of course, spend longer on each chapter/topic if you want to – read more information and gather or develop new ideas. How you use the book is up to you. Write in it, stick pictures to it, scribble notes in it, use the spaces to add images and colour – whatever helps to inspire you.

An extra notebook or journal is important as well, to write down all your thoughts, the answers to exercises and your feelings on the various issues. Writing things down is one of the best ways to really understand and to reflect on what is really happening. Note as many thoughts down as you can – they may be important later. The more you can write down, the better. It is a great motivator to re-read journals and notes to see how far you have come, because you *will* have moved on, perhaps far more than you expect right now.

Once you start to really listen to what you want, become aware of what you are thinking and feeling and take regular action, the momentum will surprise you. Your energy levels will soar and you will get far more done than you thought possible. The most important thing is that you MUST take action. Do something *every day* to make your life happier and healthier. That will be 365 actions at the end of 12 months, or three a day equals more than 1000 in a year – think what you could achieve!

For each topic you read about you will be setting goals or targets and deciding on the actions to get you there. Make them simple to start with and then we set some ambitious ones towards the end of the book.

GOAL SETTING

USE THE 'STAR' SYSTEM TO SET YOUR GOALS

 SITUATION AND SELF-AWARENESS

- What is happening currently?
- What are you happy/unhappy with?
- What frustrates you?
- What do you believe about this subject?

 TARGET/TIME

- What exactly do you want instead?
- What is your ideal goal or situation?

 ACTIONS

- What actions would move you closer to your goal?
- Which could you do this week? When exactly will you do them? What day? What time?
- Write your action plan. Put your action(s) in your diary, a notebook, or a spreadsheet to remind yourself.

 REFLECT ON THE RESULTS

- What were the results of your action plan?
- Did you complete it?
- Were the results what you wanted? If not, what could you do differently next time?

Make sure all your goals have the 'SILVER' ingredients as below.

Specific	Set measurable goals, know exactly what you want
In time	When do you want it? Set a date
Life affirming	Make sure they will make your life better, in several areas if possible
Values based	They should be congruent with your values
Ethical	They should harm no one and be legal and morally right
Robust	They must be challenging, but realistic

Let's get going on week 1

week 1 Who are *you*?

If you were to describe yourself, what would you say?

People usually identify themselves by their role in a family unit, or their job. There is much more to *you* than that!

- **What are your values?**
- **What makes your soul 'light up'?**
- **What makes you laugh?**
- **What are your strengths?**
- **What do you love to spend time doing?**

Only *you* have the particular selection of skills, talents and characteristics that makes you who you are. That is truly *amazing*.

There are some great books, websites and courses that can help you to understand yourself better. This chapter will start the process. Perhaps you feel you are in the wrong job or relationship. You are stuck in a 'rut'. You have a dream that you want to realise before it is too late. Discovering who the authentic 'you' really is, will help to identify which job, partner, friend or home would suit you best.

Getting this right can make your life happier, more exciting and extremely rewarding. Interested?

It may take time to do all the work, but it will be a journey of discovery and excitement. Once started it never stops. In total, it has taken me 40 years to get to this point, with 10 years spent reading tons of books, taking seminars, performing, laughing, meeting people and learning constantly. It has been fantastic. You will do it your own way. Your journey, like mine, will be fun, inspiring, challenging, tough and rewarding.

My life is very different and I *feel* totally different from 10 years ago and I feel more 'me' than I ever have. My real 'authentic' self is showing for the first time and I have a real optimism about the next 10, 20 and 40 years.

You can discover 'you' and feel better about who you really are, in a relatively short time. With many of my clients, it has taken about four weeks to change some of their beliefs about themselves from negative, limited beliefs, to exciting, inspiring beliefs. They begin to have real hope and optimism about their future and can then build on this to find out what it is they truly want in their lives.

One of my clients Jane, 32, recently told me that she had a feeling of happiness 'inside herself', for the first time ever. This was after only three weeks of coaching. It resulted from her accepting new ideas about herself and where her future could lie. Last year she was bored with the same job, routine, social life and living in a house she used to share with her ex-husband. She is now selling her house, applying to go to college, then on to university to train for a new vocation. She is nervous, but excited and says 'It makes you feel alive, doesn't it?'.

There are some quizzes and tests that I have found particularly useful. They helped me to discover what motivates me, or makes me feel happy. I choose to spend more time in circumstances, work and relationships that I enjoy. These exercises, and the knowledge gained from them, have changed my outlook completely.

The following websites have great self-analysis questionnaires:
www.authentichappiness.com

Discover your 'signature strengths?' How can you use these more in your work/relationships/'down' time?

www.psychologytoday.com/pto/self_tests.php

VALUES

Have you ever thought about what your values are?

I had not considered this question until I started coaching at the age of 37. No one had ever asked me. I had a certain personal code that I used for my life, but had not really thought specifically about what it was, or what it meant. Now I know my what my values are, I can choose friends, colleagues and tasks that match them. I am constantly learning about myself and as I do my values are changing too!

Your values are the standards by which you live your life now. If you have a personal conflict with another person, it may be that your values are different and therefore you find it difficult to tolerate their actions or behaviour. For example, you may expect all your dealings with others to be honest, or you may find that you work best with people who display kindness to others, or who have a sense of fun; or you may love to challenge yourself, or conversely, you may prefer to live a peaceful life. These are all values that are important to you.

Identifying your life values will help you in all sorts of situations. Others may treat people in a way that you find unpleasant, or keep you waiting for them because they are always late, or ask you to do things that you would never do willingly, or shock you with what they say about others. They may make you feel uncomfortable or angry. Notice when this happens and specifically what it was that they did or said. What do you think their values might be?

Some of your values could be:

challenge, variety, kindness, honesty, respect, love, health, openness, fun, reliability, spirituality, connection, leadership, status, justice, equality, adventure, competition, joy, freedom, integrity, wealth, success, tradition, helping others, security, innovation, authenticity.

This is a small list of possible values. It is an important exercise on which to spend time.

For a great article and an enormous list of possible values go to: **www.stevepavlina.com/articles/living-your-values-1.htm**

When your values are the same as your partner's or friends' and colleagues', you will notice that projects and communication are much easier. You will start to connect with others who have similar values. You can also change your values, by changing your behaviour. Start focusing on kindness and fun instead of status, or vice versa. See what results you get!

For example, since I have been connecting and networking with other coaches and entrepreneurs with innovative ideas about life and work, I have felt more confident about developing my own ideas.

NEEDS

Everyone has different needs outside the basic ones of food, water and shelter. Some people need to be praised, some need status, others to be entertained constantly or challenged regularly. Do you thrive on variety, security, or being alone?

I started tennis lessons a few years ago and I really enjoyed them because they gave me exercise, challenge, learning, fun and a social occasion, but most of all because my tennis coach praised us when we played our shots well. I realised that being praised, and having someone notice when I did something well, made me feel good. I started to do it more to others. Praise and compliments are a really simple way to make other people's lives more satisfying. When did you last say something to praise or truly thank another adult? Do it today and see how good you, and they, feel.

Your needs and values will often be similar to each other, but they are different. Values are the code by which you live your life. Needs are the conditions that you require to feel secure and complete in yourself.

Having unmet needs can lead to depression, anger, frustration, failed relationships and a sense of being 'out of alignment'. Recognising and meeting your needs is a great way to feel more content and to find people who can meet those needs. If you don't know what your needs are, how can your friends/partner/colleagues provide it?

Perhaps you want to be complimented more, or be thanked for what you do. You may need time alone regularly, or to meet new people each week. Think about how you would love your ideal week to be and what you would like from other people to feel totally happy. Then start to ask for it, while looking to provide others with their needs. I recommend looking at your 'need to always be right' though. That's an unhelpful one!

BELIEFS

What do you believe to be true about yourself and your abilities? What evidence is there? Does it support your belief, or contradict it? Many people have beliefs that they carry with them from childhood, or are based on others' opinions or things they have read, but which are not true and not helpful.

- 'I could never drive on the motorway.'

- 'I'll never find a man.'

- 'I couldn't earn good money in a job I really love, it's not possible.'

- 'I could never get on stage like you do and perform.'

- 'Money is evil.'

- 'I don't understand women.'

- 'I can't read a map.'

- 'I am too old to...'.

'If we all did what we were really capable of, we would astound ourselves!' THOMAS EDISON

What makes successful people different from you? They are just people, with different skills and knowledge, but most of all different *beliefs*. I have worked with some clients who have made huge changes in their lives, by changing what they believed to be true. Janine, 32, left a job in a role that conflicted with her values. She completed a course as a trainer and now has her dream job as a training and development consultant in her old industry, using creative games. She would hardly have believed this was possible a few years ago, but she is now doing it.

Client example

Beth felt that she was held back because others' reactions to her accent were negative (she was from Hong Kong) and they couldn't understand what she was saying. I was coaching her over the phone and had no trouble clearly hearing her speak excellent English, so I asked her to keep a diary of everyone that week who did understand her and those who didn't. The following week, she had a list of 38 people she had communicated with effectively and only one that was apparently finding it difficult. She laughed at this outcome and how she had let one person affect how she saw herself. I suggested the problem was not with Beth, but with the one individual who was undermining her performance.

A few years ago I never would have believed I could write a book, leap out of a plane on a parachute, support myself financially while studying performing arts, go to a comedy club and perform a five-minute spot, or be a life coach, but – here I am! As I succeed in one 'impossible' area, I look for others. The more you challenge yourself, the more you will be able to work through your fears and see other opportunities. Write down all your achievements – big or small – and start to realise what you have done already that you perhaps thought you could never do.

See if what you believe is really true. Look for evidence for and against your opinion. Find others who have achieved what you dream of. Mix with successful people. Read about amazing achievements that were assumed to be impossible.

TOP TIP – ASK BETTER QUESTIONS!

Instead of saying to yourself, 'I can't earn money doing something I really love', ask: 'How can I earn money doing something I really love?'. Notice how your brain loves a question and will try to provide an answer. Ask 'How?' and know that you can find the answer!

Coaches are trained in questioning skills and working with a coach can help you to ask yourself the right questions.

Constantly notice how you talk to yourself. Ask yourself positive questions – How can I? Who can help? What do I need to do?
Listen to the answers – use your emotions and intuition to guide you.

SKILLS AND VALUES EXERCISE

★ SITUATION AND SELF-AWARENESS

Think about how you feel about yourself at the moment. Keep a journal of all your ideas and discoveries. Read it and use it to help you see the true picture of where and who you are.

Complete a 'map of *you*'.

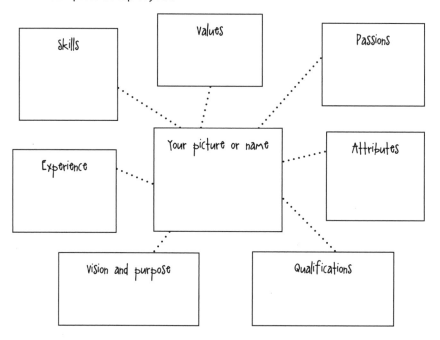

Put your name or a picture of you in the centre of a page.

Draw lines coming from the name/picture with:

- **Values** – use the website on page 7 or books to identify them.
- **Passions** – what do you truly love to do, read about, spend time and money doing, lose yourself in, do with your spare time?
- **Skills** – what you can do better than most people: communicate, sing, identify plants, match colours, diagnose illness, cook, learn?
- **Attributes** – your personal characteristics: calm, fun, open, honest, organised, natural leader?
- **Qualifications** – subjects you have some training in, whether this is professional or through courses and seminars in your own time.

- **Experience** – professional and personal: jobs, relationships, challenges, achievements?
- **Vision and purpose** – what you really want to be doing in your life.

If you do not know your skills or personal attributes, ask five people who know you well and like you, what they see as your skills and strengths – this can be a very rewarding exercise. You may be surprised.

When I asked my friends and family, communication was mentioned by everyone, with a variety of other skills and strengths. Some of these I had never considered, because I am used to them being a part of me, e.g. a good 'eye' for colour, an ability to mimic and do funny voices (I didn't say they were all useful skills!) and self-motivation.

Looking at the overall picture of who I am made me value myself and my uniqueness much more. It was also clear where there was an overlap and how all my sections were about learning, teaching, connecting with others, creativity and fun.

What have you discovered from the questions? If you haven't done them – what stops you? *How can you* complete these exercises?

TARGET OR GOAL – MAKE THEM 'SILVER' TARGETS

- What exactly do you want?
- What skills would you like to use more? Is what you do with your time in and out of work a good match to your values?
- What do you love to do, or are good at, but never find the time to do?

ACTION

- Think of all the possible and actual actions that you could do to use your skills more
- List all the ideas that you can think of. Enlist friends or a coach to help you. Which of these are you going to do?
- What simple action can you do *today* to move closer to your target? Make a phone call, meet a friend, research the subject, complete a quiz …

DO IT!

When are you going to do your others? Be specific – identify the day, time and location. Do something every day if possible. Allocate the time!

Plan for success, with one small achievable action at a time.

Do these actions for a week, then sit with your journal and …

REFLECT ON YOUR RESULTS

What worked well?

What did you enjoy?

What was difficult, but rewarding?

What did not work? Why was that? Was it up to you, or others?

Change what was less effective, then do your *new plan* for a further week. Review at the end of that week and keep refining it until you are happy with what you know. Persistent, consistent action is the key to moving forward and being successful.

This will be an ongoing project, but knowing who you truly are and becoming who you should really be is the most fun you can ever have!

 REWARD

Treat yourself to an appropriate reward.

Enjoy the reward and the feeling of moving forward.

Now to week 2 — your life balance

week 2 Your current life balance

Responses from my happynurses members shows that this is one of the main challenges in their lives – and no wonder! Working shifts, sometimes with little notice of your schedule, having to swap departments at short notice and being expected to work extra hours or work through lunch are not a great way to feel that your life is in balance!

However, you can make small changes that can all add up to you feeling like you have more control over your life. You can find the time for more happy activities and plan it into your life. You have to make it important, whatever is happening with your work and family schedule. Read on for a great tool to help you start…

To help identify the areas that will be the most important for you to focus on for the 12-week action plan, a useful tool to help you is the 'Wheel of Life'. You may have seen this before in articles or books. I think its simplicity is its strong point and I have used one every 12 weeks for the past three years to assess how my life is doing and to set my actions for each week to ensure that I reach my 12-week targets and goals. Many of my clients find it a useful starting point too.

Using it can highlight imbalances in your life, or make you think about areas of your life that you have been ignoring. There are no right or wrong answers. The important thing is to spend time thinking about each area and to be honest about how content you are with each one. Give each area a score out of 10 to indicate how happy you are with that area at the current time.

Then be bold! – what would make that area a '10 out of 10' score? What would be the *best* thing for your psychological well-being regarding money, work or family relationships?

This is to challenge you to think about what you *really* want for yourself in your life. Think big. If you feel that 'something is missing', then this simple exercise can help to point to what that may be.

Draw a circle on a big piece of paper. Divide it into six or eight segments. Have one segment for each area of your life.

These are the areas in my wheel. Yours may be different, but there will be about six to eight.

WHEEL OF LIFE

Health – physical and psychological

Work – do you like your job; does it 'suit you'?

Money – income versus spending and debts

Friends and social – your circle of friends and social life

Family – your family, partner, parents, pets

Home – town, area, house/flat

Fun, challenge and excitement – travel, performing, hobbies

Development and learning – spirituality/community

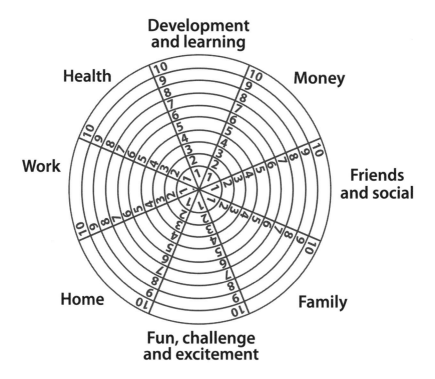

Any other sections you wish to include, or to leave out, are OK. It is your individual plan. However, do not exclude items that are too difficult to think about. If you feel stressed thinking about them, leave them in, score them and return when you feel better able to tackle them. With a firmer foundation of better health, supportive friends and a comfortable home you will feel stronger and more able to confront difficult challenges.

You can organise this information in a way that suits you. You can use a journal/ notebook or A4 papers in a funky file, or a spreadsheet – it's up to you.

When I started to do the exercises 10 years ago I used an A4 ring binder to hold the information for each section, added pictures from magazines and used lots of colours. I still use a similar system in an A5 notebook – my 12-week action book – as this works for me. Put it on whatever format you like to use, as long as you look at it regularly (daily is best), write lots of information in it and use it to inspire you.

When you have identified one action for each section that will move you closer to your ultimate goal, decide exactly *when* you will do it – the sooner the better – then do it!! It can be as simple as buying a health magazine this afternoon, eating an extra piece of fruit each day this week, phoning an old friend for a chat, looking in an estate agent's window, taking your child to the cinema – whatever is right for you. Do it today, or at least this week. Make a start!

While you work through the rest of the book, focus on the 'wheel' and refer back to it. Use the 'STAR' pages to move you away from your current situation, towards your better/best one. None of this book will work without *action*. You can work through with a coach or a friend, which will help. With the first coaching book that I borrowed, I worked through the exercises with one of my sisters and it was very helpful to share our experiences, motivate each other and have someone to be accountable to.

USING THE WHEEL TO CREATE A HAPPYLIFE – MY STORY

My 'wheel of life' three years ago, was so empty it had tumbleweed blowing through it! I had experienced bereavement, depression and had given up a job that I hated, which included a stressful and soul-destroying commute, but without a permanent job to replace it. I had attempted to launch a coaching practice but rather half-heartedly and without the support I needed and this had wrecked my confidence and self-esteem. I used a great therapist to help lift me out of my depression, got emotional and practical support from my wonderful family and then looked at my current life.

Most of the sections on my 'wheel' scored a 1 or 2. I used my coaching knowledge to build myself a more balanced and meaningful life. I identified small, manageable actions to take me to where I wanted to be

in 12 weeks. It seemed a huge task to think about all the changes, but breaking it down to daily and weekly actions was less stressful and meant that I achieved most of my goals. I wrote the actions that I needed to take in a lovely A5 notebook and ticked them off when I had done them. A walk of 5,000 steps, posting a card to a friend, filling in an application form, watching a DVD all 'counted'. Making lists and ticking off actions when completed worked for me, as well as lots of rewards – find what works for you.

For example, I knew that I needed to sell my house. This was a difficult issue, as it had been my home for 10 years. I had no idea how to do it. I had never been through the process before. I initially made a list of why I should stay and why I should move, which illustrated that the benefits of moving far outweighed those of staying, especially when I started my new job 40 miles away.

I initially set myself the small action of walking into an estate agent and talking about getting my house valued. The first step. That was all.

I felt great having achieved this step and wanted to use the momentum and small increase in confidence, having done this one thing, to keep me moving towards my goal. I liked the agent very much and decided to get as many of the preliminaries done as soon as possible.

I knew that making a quick decision would be less stressful for me. I had confidence in him and trusted my judgement, so I followed his guidance, signed up and got my house on the market. Financially this may not have been the smartest move (I never compared, so I don't know), but I was happy with making a quick decision. This left time and energy for actions in other sections of my life.

My health section also needed attention, so after researching on the Internet, I embarked on a low GI diet – lots of fibre, fruit, nuts and veg. It was based on foods I liked and allowed me to have three meals and snacks a day – what a bonus! I gave up alcohol, joined a gym, bought a pedometer and walked most days. These small, manageable steps all inspired me and made me feel healthier. After a couple of weeks my health 'actions' were simply to maintain what I was doing – with small increases in the amount of exercise – establishing new healthy habits.

I drew up a weight chart to show my progress. This was a great help, as even small losses showed that the 'trend' was downhill!

There were similar small, easy actions for all areas, which have meant that a few years later most of the sections of my 'wheel' score 7 or more. Wow! What an improvement! The process worked so well, I still do it each week and set actions based on my goals – hence this book.

I got a new job which I enjoyed, moved to a beautiful flat in a new town, made new friends, maintained links with a lot of my old ones, stayed fit, developed an expanding social life. I also travelled to new places, started coaching again and have now launched **www.happynurses.co.uk**! It has been a gradual process, using consistent small actions to move forward, even when I was scared, uncomfortable and unsure.

I invite you now to spend an hour or so to make a list of everything you want to *be*, everything you want to *do* and everything you want to *have* – go wild and be big and bold in your ideas!

For example, I have some outlandish ideas, but ones I can mention here are: finish writing this book in 12 weeks; run creative, playful workshops for nurses on health and coaching issues; learn to surf; sing with a 'swing' band; meet Robbie Williams; return to Australia; perform 'stand-up' comedy; tour Devon and Cornwall in a camper van; fly over the Grand Canyon (obviously in some sort of plane or helicopter!).

I have performed stand-up comedy now, so that one has been 'ticked off' the list and I am starting to run workshops and some of the other activities that were just 'ideas' or 'dreams' a few months or years ago. Check my progress on **www.happynurses.co.uk**!

Don't censor your thoughts, let your imagination flow and when you have filled a couple of sheets of paper with ideas, see which ones really inspire and excite you. Even one hour a week doing something you really love will help you to find more happiness in life. One hour singing a week started the total overhaul of my own life! Make sure you make it important enough that it is always in the schedule and others help and support you in taking 'time out'.

A list like this can be a great motivator – some will be big dreams, other things you can achieve this year, or even today! You could sign up for a course, phone a college, talk to an expert, join a dating agency, invite someone you would like to know better to have coffee, book a flight, get a brochure, surf the 'net for information.

DO SOMETHING!

Dream big dreams… some of it will happen, but only if you take action!

STAR – write all your ideas in a notebook or journal. No denial or delusion or being hard on yourself, just the bare facts.

This is your starting point.

 SITUATION AND SELF-AWARENESS

- Think about how your life balance is at the moment.
- Complete the 'wheel of life' and fill it in. Be honest!
- What have you discovered from the exercise?

 TARGET OR GOAL – MAKE THEM 'SILVER' TARGETS

- How do you want your life balance to be instead?
- What exactly do you want in your life and when?
- What would be your ultimate 10 out of 10, amazing 'goal' or target for each section?

 ACTION – POSSIBLE AND ACTUAL

- List all the ideas you can think of to improve each area of your life, enlist friends, partner or a coach to help you.
- Which of these are you going to do?
- What simple action can you do *today* to move closer to your target?
- *Do it*! Do one action for each section.
- Feel the excitement and satisfaction of taking control and moving forward.
- Every week I write at least one action for each area of my 'wheel'. This keeps my life moving forward. They can be relatively small, but they must be done – thinking alone does not change things, nor planning, only action – that's how it is!

 REFLECTION – YOUR RESULTS

What worked well? What did you learn?

What was difficult, but rewarding?

What did not work? Why was that? Was it up to you, or others?

 REWARD

Treat yourself to an appropriate reward. Enjoy the reward and the feeling of success.

Well done, now keep this up each week while we look at your health.

week 3 How healthy are you?

Let's make a start by discovering how healthy you feel *now*. This chapter has lots of activities in it, as you need to establish healthy habits to get you to the end of the book and to achieve any ambitious goals you will set.

Your health is affected by many factors – your relationships, habits, environment and amount of stress you experience amongst others. Making positive changes in all these areas will lead to improvements.

Be honest when you answer the questions in this chapter, as only *you* will see this information and a true appraisal of where you are *now* will ensure the best results.

- *How energetic do you feel?*
- *Are you happy with your mental and physical health?*
- *Do you have 'niggling' problems that need taking care of?*

True health is more than just what you eat, or how often you go to the gym. The idea of holistic health has expanded in recent years, with many health professionals considering the 'whole person' and their lifestyle in their treatment. No single item can be isolated from the others. So, complete the following exercise to see where you are today with regard to your health.

Use the 'health chart' on p20 and decide how satisfied you are now with these aspects of your health and well-being.

Answer with yes/sometimes/never. Be honest, write down your answers, then see how you feel about what you have written.

Health Chart	Yes	Sometimes	Never
Diet			
I eat at least five portions of fruit and veg a day.			
I rarely eat sugary, fatty or junk foods.			
Fluids			
I drink at least a litre of water a day.			
I rarely drink alcohol, sugary or caffeinated drinks.			
Activity			
I am active for at least 20 to 30 minutes daily – sports/walking/dancing/aerobic activity/stretching. I feel fit.			
Sleep			
I sleep well every night. My bedroom is relaxing and tranquil.			
Body maintenance			
I visit the dentist and optician regularly and have complementary therapy when needed.			
Psychological health			
I feel confident and optimistic about my future. I have exciting projects I am working towards.			
Relationships			
I love myself and have loving friends and family. I feel part of a supportive community.			
Happiness			
I do something each day that makes me truly happy.			
Stress			
I feel relaxed and able to cope most of the time.			
I never use caffeine, tobacco, marijuana, drugs or food to cope with stress.			

HEALTH QUESTIONS TO STIMULATE THOUGHTS

Write down your answers, ideas, questions and inspirations
as you go through the list.

 CURRENT REALITY – BODY IMAGE

- What do I like about my body?
- What are my best feature/s
- On what do I get complimented?
- How do I feel when I look at myself in the morning?
- Do I avoid looking at myself?
- Do I get positive feedback?
- How often do I get complimented?
- Who compliments me?
- Who criticises me?
- What do they criticise about me?
- Are they 'right'? What evidence is there?
- What physical skills do I have?
- What is the best physical skill I have?
- When have I felt happiest about my body and why?
- What was the worst and why?

 HOW DO YOU FEEL ABOUT EXERCISE AND ACTIVITY?

- I love it!
- It's challenging
- It's boring
- I make friends doing it
- It costs too much money
- I don't have time
- It's fun!
- It interrupts my week
- I do it for self-respect/self esteem
- I can't be bothered, it's too hard
- I don't know how to get started
- Others expect me to do it

- It's what everyone does
- No one I know keeps themselves fit and healthy.

 HOW DO YOU FEEL ABOUT YOUR CURRENT HEALTH HABITS?

- I smoke too much
- I drink too much
- I'm bored
- I need a change
- I wish I could get started
- I enjoy it at times
- There are aspects I love and aspects I hate
- I don't know what I would do differently
- I eat too much
- I eat the wrong things
- I eat because I am bored/stressed/lonely
- My partner doesn't support me
- I've tried and failed too many times already
- I hate myself for failing.

 IDEAL, HEALTHY LIFE

- Who would I exercise, or be active, with?
- How much activity time could I fit into my week?
- What food would I eat?
- How often would I smoke/drink alcohol?
- What treats would I have?
- What compliments would I receive?
- How would I look? What would I wear?
- How would I like to feel about myself/my body?
- How would I get healthy? Alone, with one other, or in a group?
- Who do I know who is happy with their health?
- Whose health would I like to have/have I been interested in?
- What events would I like to be able to take part in?
- What other benefits would being healthy have for my life?

PRACTICALITIES AND CREATIVE THINKING

- Who could I ask for help?
- Where can I get information from?
- What books/magazines/journals do I read?
- What TV programmes inspire me?
- What active hobbies do I have, or would I like to try?
- How do I have fun with my body?
- What physical activities have you enjoyed as a child/young adult?
- Ask others what they think your physical skills are
- Who do I admire? Why?
- What physical activities make me lose track of time?
- If I had unlimited money, what would I do to improve my health?

Taking responsibility for factors that you *can* control *now* is a great start. Only you can do it, it is up to you.

Having worked as a nurse for over 20 years, I have seen many people of all ages suffer disabilities and diseases with a reduced quality of life, and I am sure you have too! I would recommend being as healthy as possible for as long as possible! Some of these problems were preventable if the individuals had made different decisions about how they treated their bodies. It is a precious thing – once your body no longer works, 'you' will have nowhere to live.

There are some exceptional people who have been profoundly affected by ill-health, raising awareness for diseases, or money for treatment and charitable causes; for example, Christopher Reeve, Michael J Fox, Roy Castle, Jane Tomlinson, as well as many individuals I have met through my profession who have set up charities closer to home. They have made the best of the situation and suffering illness, or losing a loved one, has taught them some life lessons that have changed them as a person.

However, it is easier to achieve your life goals if you are physically and mentally well. Taking care of your health does not have to be difficult and can affect how you feel every minute of every day. You can wake up feeling refreshed and enthusiastic. You will cope more easily with stress, enjoy physical activities, play for longer with your children or grandchildren, or even see the view from the top of a high mountain after walking up it!

You should even live longer – quality and quantity – a win-win situation.

Feeling healthier and fitter will help you to achieve your goals. Achieving your goals will make you happier and more energised. It all fits together perfectly. First, we need a strong foundation for health, including physical and psychological factors.

Look at your body from top to toe and consider areas that are working well. The 'body beautiful' is all very well, but the 'body functional' is far more important. If it all works efficiently, you have a great foundation for healthy changes. If there are issues which need a professional to treat – muscles, teeth, skin or spine – get help *this week*. Hoping niggles will go away won't work – I have tried it and many of my patients have at some point too.

Simple changes can have amazing effects. If you watched 'You Are What You Eat' or 'Honey, We're Killing the Kids' on TV, you can see the effect that healthier foods have on the well-being of the participants. Bland, processed junk foods (the clue is in the name!) are replaced by fresh, varied diets and the individuals look brighter and sleep better. They lose weight and have more confidence and self-esteem (I shall not mention what happens to their poo!). Breaking addictions to caffeinated drinks, alcohol, sugary foods and fizzy drinks can also make a profound difference to how they feel emotionally and physically.

Buying recipe books, fitness DVDs and magazines and putting them on your shelves will not make you fit and healthy – I've tried this too! The only results are from *action*. The more you do, the easier it becomes.

If you have a chronic condition, make sure you know what you are doing to promote your body and improve your long-term health – use the Internet for information from charities and societies that can answer your questions. Be your own health guru! Know what is helping, and what is hindering your well-being. You are responsible for your health and looking after the body that you live in – take loving care of it the same way you would your children or someone else you loved dearly.

Start this week, by looking at easy steps to improve how you treat your physical body

PHYSICAL HEALTH

FOOD, FLUIDS AND DRUG USE

What you put into your body is vitally important in how you feel. You literally are 'what you eat'. Your body constructs new cells out of the products that you feed it and its job is much more efficient with nutritious food, water and fresh air, instead of fatty, additive laden food, cigarettes and alcohol.

The most important actions you can do are:

- Give up smoking.
- Stop using drugs (legal and illegal) and food as a prop for your life. This includes the excessive use of alcohol.
- Lose weight so that your body mass is within the healthy range for your height.

These will have the greatest impact on your daily health and reduce your risk of disease and disability.

There are professional groups and individuals available to help you lose weight, get fitter, or reduce your alcohol intake. It can be difficult to give up these items without seeking help. Get serious, set a target and find the support to assist you through the process.

Where to get help

UK – Use your GP, or local 'walk in clinic'. They may have specialist nurses to help you.

Several of my clients have had other health issues that needed to be challenged. Some of them have used professionals – a personal trainer for exercise ideas, a therapist for emotional issues around eating and complementary therapists for back and muscle problems and relaxation. Others have set their own agenda, assessing what action would suit them best and reviewing their progress to ensure continued success.

Writing everything down is one of the most helpful activities you can do to help understand where you are now and your starting point for change. It can illustrate clearly *exactly* what is really happening, rather than your 'wishful thinking'. Denial can be an important factor in your continued failure. How much and what, do you *really* eat? How much alcohol have you *really* drunk this week? How do you feel when you see it actually written down?

Client example

Keeping a food diary can highlight exactly what and when you eat. Becky, 34, started having coaching when she was overweight, unfit and drinking too much alcohol. She had started to make changes to her diet, adding lower GI foods and becoming aware of what she actually ate and drank – there was no more denial. She kept a food and drinks diary for her weekend, which was the time in the week that she found it harder to stick to her routine. She thought she had done 'quite well'.

Her therapist, however, was shocked by the amount of alcohol she consumed and her erratic eating habits. He was not at all surprised by her feelings of lethargy and ongoing weight problems, based on what he read on the pages. Her view of what a healthy, energising diet was challenged and has now improved, having had a specialist look at what she ate and drank.

Susan, 32, the mother of two small children, found that her snacking was a problem, especially at times when her children were eating. We brainstormed all the items that would feel like a treat to her, but were healthy and lower in calories than the snacks she had been having. She decided she would have a low-calorie fizzy mixer with juice, or tropical fruit, as her treat.

STAR ACTIONS EXAMPLE

SITUATION

Claire was drinking alcohol every day, in unhealthy quantities and wanted to cut down to a healthy weekly limit.

TARGET OR GOAL – MAKE THEM 'SILVER' TARGETS

Initially to drink *no* alcohol for a week to break the habit

ACTIONS

To refuse any alcohol offered, avoid temptation initially by not going to bars, pubs etc and stock up with other nice drinks.

REFLECTION

Claire successfully completed a week. It was a challenge, but it got easier and she carried on for another week. Eventually Claire didn't drink alcohol for 18 months.

This was me! My initial target was not to give up for 18 months, just a week.

If a big goal seems too difficult, then setting a small target can lead on to achieving bigger goals. Breaking bad habits can be the hardest part of making health changes. If it seems easier for you, commit to something for a day only, then a week, then review your achievements at the end of each week. Change your actions if you were unsuccessful and keep going if it worked. What got in the way? What events made it

difficult? Plan for those next time. Have alternative ideas. Find a plan you can stick to long term and do it a day at a time. Aim for long term good habits, not quick results.

Client ideas

- Use smaller plates to eat from, instead of filling a large plate.

- Eat five fruit and veg a day; record all input to keep to target.

- Drink more water by setting a target of three 500ml bottles a day.

- Keep fruit and water by the bed to start the day, then go straight to the gym or for a walk in the morning.

- Plan for times in hotels/holidays/ parties in advance.

- Always have water and dried or fresh fruit with you to reduce binges.

- If you want to eat more fruit you have to buy more of it!

- Dancing counts as exercise – salsa, jive, ceroc. It's fun, sociable and healthy.

- Set a walking target for the week, every little bit counts. Measure steps, time, circuits or distance – whichever suits you.

- Use fitness and slimming magazines for inspiration.

- Create an 'image board' with photos to inspire you.

PHYSICAL ACTIVITY

Keeping your body active helps you to look and feel young, achieves and maintains a healthy weight, builds muscle and bone mass and keeps your heart healthy. You can be active at any age and finding something you enjoy, setting targets and being consistent are the best ways to maintain fitness. I have played tennis with 80 year olds who still enjoyed the game, and have walked with my 75 year old grandmother. Some of my great-aunts are still active walkers in their 90s.

How active are you? Do you exercise regularly? What did you learn from the questions in the first section?

Starting a programme is usually the hardest part. Once you have been more active for a few weeks, you begin to feel the benefits. You find the activity easier, feel more energetic and probably receive compliments which will make it easier to keep going. It will become a habit within 30 days. If you need help to get started talk to a personal trainer, join a gym, a dance class, or start a walking group with other people.

Client example

Lizzie wanted to get fitter. She initially set a target of running a 5km race, but with further exploration she decided what she really wanted was to walk for fitness, as she enjoyed it. She set an initial walking target, of a certain number of steps, for the week. Her initial target was unrealistic – she had a tendency to set targets that were too ambitious and then fail. This would lead her to 'give up' completely (sound familiar?).

We reduced the weekly total of steps to a manageable, but still challenging, total. Two weeks later, she reviewed her results and decided the target should be the total number of hours instead. She also felt that even 15 or 20 minutes walking would count towards the total, rather than only walks of at least an hour. It made it easier to fit into her schedule and more manageable physically. It also meant that not having her pedometer was no longer an excuse to miss a walk.

Her action plan suited her and was refined over a couple of weeks to be easier to monitor and achieve. If you do not achieve your target – look at what you did and what stopped it from working. Change what you do next week and review again, You will come to the best solution for you. Do something you enjoy doing!

What small actions could you implement as a start this week to boost your physical health?

TAKE SMALL STEPS AND KEEP GOING!

STAR ACTIONS

SITUATION AND SELF-AWARENESS

Think about how you feel about your physical health at the moment.

What are your good habits? What are your unhealthy habits? Note down what you eat and drink for a week and why. What specific times do you overeat/drink/ smoke? How could you manage these in a different way?

TARGET OR GOAL – MAKE THEM 'SILVER' TARGETS

What do you want instead?

What size would you like to be? How do you want to look? How do you want to 'feel' in your body?

Believe it is possible!

ACTION – AVAILABLE AND ACTUAL

List all the ideas you can think of – enlist a personal trainer, instructor, nutritionist, therapist or a coach to help you.

Use health websites and magazines for extra ideas.

Which of these actions are you going to do?

What simple action can you do *today* to move closer to your target?

DO IT!

When are you going to do your others? Be specific – day, time, location.

Plan for success – do smaller actions successfully.

Consistent action is the key to lasting change.

Record everything you think and do for a week, then:

REFLECTION – RESULTS AT THE END OF A WEEK

What worked well?

What did you enjoy?

What was difficult, but rewarding?

What did not work?

Why was that?

Was it up to you, or others?

Alter your plan for the next week, then start again and keep going, review at the end of this week, then refine your plan again.

Small incremental steps that are right for *you* are vital.

REWARD

Treat yourself to a positive health reward, a massage, pedicure, or a day at the coast.

BOOKS

Beat the Booze, Edmund and Helen Tirbutt. Harriman House Ltd, 2008.

The Food Doctor Everyday Diet, Dr Ian Marber. Dorling Kindersley, 2005.

For organic fruit and veg direct to your home:
www.abelandcole.com
www.riverfordorganics.com

MAGAZINES

Zest, *Natural Health*, or *Health and Fitness* for some fitness inspiration

Next we will look at your home and how it can influence your psychological well-being.

week 4 **Your environment**

Where you live can seriously affect your psychological and physical health, so it is crucial to assess whether it is 'right' for you. If not, what can do you about it?

Your 'wheel of life' in Chapter 2 will have contained your home or surroundings as one of the sections. What did you identify that you liked about where you live and what could be better?

You should consider everything from the town or city you live in, the view from your bedroom, to the colour of the walls in the lounge, or the amount of clutter in the hall.

- *Do you like your town/city?*
- *Is the area safe and clean?*
- *Does your house or flat suit you?*
- *Do you enjoy living there?*
- *Are the rooms tidy and well decorated?*
- *Do you relax there?*
- *Can you invite friends round?*

Three years ago I was living in a city I loved, but was bored with. I owned a house that wasn't where I wanted to live, in a street I didn't like any more. Not good. However, I couldn't imagine myself living anywhere else, as I had been there for 10 years. I started changing my thoughts by noting what I liked about other people's homes and surroundings and making a list of my 'ideal' home and imagining myself living in some of these places. They were nothing like where I currently lived and I began to expand my ideas of where I *could* live.

I now live in a flat that is 95% what I would want. I love living here and feel grateful every morning when I look at the view of the park. I felt really comfortable here after only a couple of weeks. It wasn't an easy process to move and took three buyers and nine months to eventually complete the sale. It was worth the stress and effort, however, to be where I am now.

Many of my visitors mention how much it 'suits' me. Does your home suit you, or reflect who you are? It is easy to make a choice and then feel stuck with it – you are not stuck with anything in life! I do want to live by the sea, and visualise this outcome regularly until I am in a position to do it for real. You can do the same. Mentally create the place where you would love to live and spend time stepping into your 'picture' of it.

What would you really want from the place where you live? Can you get that in your current home without moving – redecorate, tidy up, get de-cluttering professionals in, move things round?

There is real freedom in getting rid of items that you don't use, need or like any more. TV programmes highlight the money that can be made from selling some old items. Or you can give them away to charity, sell them on an online auction, or invite friends round for a sale or swap. There are online groups for 'recycling' items too. Selling old items can fund the purchase of new ones, or be invested.

QUESTIONS TO STIMULATE THOUGHTS

Write down your answers, ideas, questions and inspirations as you go through the list.

CURRENT REALITY

- What do I like about my home?
- How do I feel when I look at my home?
- Do I avoid looking around where I live?
- What DIY/decorating/cleaning skills do I have?
- What was the best place I ever lived, and why?
- What was the worst, and why?

HOW DO YOU FEEL ABOUT YOUR HOME ENVIRONMENT?

- I love it!
- I hate living here
- It costs too much money
- I don't have time to look after it/keep it clean
- I can't be bothered to look after it
- I don't know how to change it
- Others expect me to do all the work, they don't help
- The neighbourhood has got worse/feels unsafe/is noisy
- I hate the view from the windows
- I never liked this house/flat
- I need a change

- Some of it is just right and other parts need work
- I wish I could get started
- I don't know what I would do differently
- I am too isolated
- I don't like this town
- My partner doesn't support me
- My family are unhappy here
- The home is too crowded.

IDEAL HOME

- Where would I love to live?
- How much space would I like?
- How would I like my home to look?
- Who do I know who is happy with their home?
- Whose home would I like to have/have I been interested in?
- What do I like about their home?
- What would I do to make my home nicer to live in?
- If I liked my home, in what other ways would I feel different?

PRACTICALITIES AND CREATIVE THINKING

- Who could I ask for help?
- Where can I get information from?
- What books/magazines/journals do I read?
- What TV programmes do I feel inspired by?
- What decorating skills do I have?
- What could I do for very little money, to start the process?
- What colours/styles do I like?
- What do my family/partner think?
- Do we agree?
- How can we all be happy with it?
- If I had unlimited money, what would I do with my home?

'De-cluttering' is a word that has now entered the common vocabulary thanks to TV programmes and magazine articles. Getting rid of physical 'stuff' can really help with mental clarity, even though it can be a challenge emotionally. If you have never tried it, I highly recommend doing it. For example, it is estimated that people wear 20% of their clothes 80% of the time. So you could get rid of 80% of the items in your wardrobe and not really miss them! It is also easier and quicker in the mornings to have fewer choices.

The same principle can be used for all areas in the house. Get rid of items that you don't need or use regularly – toys that the children have grown out of, clothes that don't fit them, gifts that you have never liked! This can provide a real sense of mental space, as well as physical room in your home. Decide when you have time to do it, make a commitment to do it and get on with it. Some music can help – with a funky beat to help the work along. Involve friends and family and make it fun. Reward yourselves when it is done!

Treat yourself to a space in your home where you can really relax. Keep the bedroom for sleep and nocturnal activity – not work, study or storage of junk. Find a way to maximise space and storage and feel the difference. Clients who start to look after their homes begin to look after themselves more too. Your home is a reflection of the way that you feel.

Client example

Meg, 41, has three children, takes foreign students in as lodgers and came to me for coaching on her self-esteem and health issues. In discussing her current situation, she identified that she was feeling 'overwhelmed' and out of control. She felt disorganised and constantly chasing the next chore to be done. Her action plan for the first week was to do one job each day that would clear her physical environment and give her more mental space. She thought of seven jobs that really needed doing and committed to completing one each day – clearing the ironing pile, tidying the paperwork in the office and sorting out the garden.

We looked at ways to make these jobs fun for her – involving her family, rewards afterwards, playing music, listening to a personal development tape. There is always room for fun! The following week, she felt totally different and her voice sounded more excited and she laughed much more. She had also thought of lots of new ideas for her life. This all started by tidying her environment.

You can cut down on telephone and postal clutter straight away and register for the telephone and postal preference service (www.tps.com and www.mps.com). This will remove junk mail and cold calling from your life. Bliss.

STAR ACTIONS

SITUATION AND SELF-AWARENESS

Focus on how you feel about your home at the moment.

Where do you live? How do you describe your town and home?

What have you discovered from the questions?

TARGET OR GOAL – MAKE THEM 'SILVER' TARGETS

What exactly do you want instead? Look at pictures and really imagine your dream home in a lovely town or village, or even another country, if that is where you would really like to live. Write all your ideas down, no matter what they are. Stick pictures of homes you love in your journal, look in estate agents' windows or on property websites and start to dream.

ACTION – AVAILABLE AND ACTUAL

List all the ideas you can think of to help you – enlist friends, a decorator, interior designer, estate agent, books, websites and magazines.

Which of these are you going to do? What simple action can you do *today* to move closer to your target?

DO IT!

When are you going to do your others? Be specific – day, time, location.

Plan for success – do smaller actions successfully.

REFLECTION ON YOUR RESULTS AND THOUGHTS

What worked well? What ideas did you have that you tried?

What did you enjoy? What was difficult, but rewarding?

What did not work? Why was that?

Was it up to you, or others?

What do you need to do this week to move things one step nearer your dream? Keep going. Often people fail to achieve their dreams because they give up too early.

Next we will look at your work, so have a break and write down your thoughts, then let's go!

week 5 Work and career – enjoy earning money!

How does that title grab you? Do you believe that you can enjoy earning money?

Is work a drudge for you? Or is your job a source of pleasure, fulfilment and personal development? Do you think that is a ridiculous question because 'Of course it isn't …'

Would you like to have a job or business that allows you to develop as your 'true authentic self', live life to your values and have fun at the same time?

If so, then read on. It needn't mean a career change – although it may if you and your job are a poor match as far as intellect, skills, personality, interests and values are concerned.

You can start to change your *attitude* to your current job and feel more positive if you change what you do and how you perceive your current job. Look at what you enjoy in your current role. Which skills do you like to use? What knowledge do you enjoy using?

For example the book *Fish! Tales* is an inspirational read from beginning to end. It highlights simple actions that helped individuals to enjoy their jobs, have fun and gain more satisfaction.

 BOOKS

FISH! Tales, Stephen Lundin, John Christensen, Harry Paul. Hodder and Stoughton, 2003.

If you are thinking of a career move, or need new inspiration, remember that you do not have to stay where you stay until you retire! Think of how many years you have left at work – is this what you really want? Look at your boss or manager – do you want to be them? If you do then – well done! If not, read on …

If you think "But I have always done this, I wouldn't know what else to do", you can find out if you give some time and effort to the project. Think about yourself as a person, rather than as an employee. Look at your answers in chapters 2 and 3. Revisit the 'map of you'. Focus on your values, what activities and surroundings make you feel happy and give you a sense of achievement.

Client example (Rachel, 32, dental nurse)

Situation	I am in an unfulfilling job, I find it really boring. I got into this career a few years ago and it was never really what I wanted to do.
Target	To find a career that I would find rewarding and exciting.
Actions	I will complete the skills test, look at the conditions I would like at work and identify a new direction.
Results	I completed the questions and self-analysis, chose a course that I am really interested in at college. I am interested in helping other people and doing a rewarding job. I like fashion, beauty and am attracted to media, performing, social care and fashion as areas of interest. I would love a job where I make a real difference.
	I have been offered two new jobs, unexpectedly, as a dental nurse in different practices. I have accepted the most exciting one, with advanced skills to provide a different routine and new colleagues while I explore college courses and plan my next step.

Rachel is now at university studying for a new career as an occupational therapist!

You are not stuck!

It may take time, but you *can* change your employer, career, routine and situation. I have done it several times, as have many of my clients, once they thought about it as a real possibility and *planned* it.

I would not recommend doing what I did in 2000 – resigning from my Sister's post with no plan – although it did make me find out another way to live, as I *had* to. Get help and support from a great life or career coach, supportive friends and family and create a plan for change.

CAREER COACHING QUESTIONS

Write down your answers, ideas, thoughts, questions and inspirations as you go through the list:

 CURRENT REALITY

- How long have I been doing my job?
- Why did I do this particular job?
- What do I like about my job?
- How do I feel going to work in the morning?

- Who do I work with?
- Do I have friends at work?
- Do I get positive feedback?
- How often do I get thanked at work?
- What skills do I enjoy using in my job?
- What is the best aspect of my job?
- Does my salary pay my bills?
- What was the best day I ever had at work, why?
- What was the worst and why?

? WHY DO YOU WORK?

- I love it!
- For the challenge
- To relieve boredom
- Friendship
- I need the money
- To provide status
- For fun!
- Structures my week
- Self-respect
- Personal development
- To make a difference/contribution
- I don't know how else to fill the time
- Others expect me to work
- It's what everyone does.

HOW DO YOU FEEL ABOUT YOUR CURRENT JOB?

- I love it!
- I hate it!
- I'm bored
- I need a change
- I wish I'd never done it
- I enjoy it at times
- There are aspects I love and aspects I hate

- I don't know what else I would do.

YOUR 'IDEAL' JOB – QUESTIONS TO STIMULATE IDEAS

- Who would you work with?
- What hours would you work?
- How much would you earn?
- Would you work with people/ideas/things?
- What bonuses or perks would you want?
- Who do you know who is happy in their work?
- Whose job have you been interested in?
- What business would you set up, if there were no obstacles?

PRACTICALITIES AND CREATIVE THINKING

- Would you relocate?
- Would you retrain/study further?
- Who could you ask for help?
- Where can you get information from?
- What books/magazines/journals do you read?
- What TV programmes do you feel inspired by?
- What hobbies do you have?
- What makes you feel excited, challenged?
- How do you have fun?
- What would you do, even if you weren't paid for it?
- Who do you like spending time with?
- Would you rather work alone? From home?
- What did you love to do when you were seven years old?
- What subject do you love to talk about?
- What skills do you have? List them …
- What talents do you have? List them …
- Ask others what they think your skills are
- Who do you admire?
- What are you doing when you lose track of time?
- If you had unlimited money, what would you do with your life?
- If you could do *anything*, what would that be?

What is your secret dream? … be bold, brave, unlimited!

All my clients have had ideas that were 'buried', perhaps because of disapproval from others, or the feeling that it was a silly, or unrealistic thing to want.

Client example

Daniel was looking for direction in his work. He had done a number of unskilled jobs since college and at the age of 30 was bored and unsatisfied. I could see that he had great potential, which had been unrecognised up to now. Over the course of six coaching sessions we explored his attitudes to work, the specific aspects of his jobs he had enjoyed and which aspects of working he had not. I asked him what skills he had and there was a long silence. He could not think of any, as no one had ever asked him before.

I set him an exercise to ask five people who knew him well what they thought his 'best skills' were. We also looked at activities and hobbies that he really enjoyed, both now and in the past, and what interested and excited him.

Some of the aspects were specific – he liked to work outside, in a small team of people. Others were more general – he liked to create something, he liked variety, he enjoyed working regular hours. When he was younger he loved to be outside, digging in the soil for hours.

He accessed job ideas via his local career office and thought more about the type of environment and conditions he would like to work in. For the first three weeks his thoughts kept returning to the brewery business, which was an area he had worked in previously, his 'comfort zone'.

In week five there was a breakthrough when he looked at all the information he had collected and decided that he wanted to be a gardener. It was an excellent match. He applied for a course at his local college and attended one day a week. He then started gardening jobs alongside his studies and now, a few years later, has a successful and rewarding career in horticulture.

Thinking back to what you enjoyed doing as a child, or love to do as a hobby can be the first step in realising that what you do to earn money can be different. Perhaps re-training would be a good investment into the next 30 years of your work life. There are many ways of doing this – evening and day classes, distance and e-courses, the Open University, ICS (International Correspondance Schools) and other providers.

Explore career alternatives, or discover more about a good match for you:
www.jobsetc.ca
www.assessment.com
www.career-changers.com
www.authentichappiness.org – Do the signature strengths test if you haven't already.

You may already have an idea for a business. Get advice, help, inspiration from business experts and start-up websites. Many skills that you use in your nursing role can be useful working for yourself or in another environment.

It is possible to make money doing something that you love to do and you could even be the first person to create something unique. I have wanted to combine nursing, performing and coaching for years, but could not see how, until I am doing it now through **happynurses**! Writing was never on my list, but I really enjoy it and it is another way to share my expertise, teach, learn, communicate and earn money. Be open to all sorts of ideas.

You could run a small business alongside a regular job, or start an Internet-based business. You can have a 'portfolio' career with many different strands and sources of income. Speaking, writing, teaching, nursing, selling crafts, singing, coaching, comedy, selling products, using your hobby to create income, getting started with MLM (multi-level marketing) products or use your communication skills to assist others.

For more information on business see:

www.businesslink.co.uk

www.beermat.biz

STAR ACTION PAGES

SITUATION AND SELF-AWARENESS

Think about how you feel about your work at the moment.

What have you discovered from the questions in the exercises earlier in the chapter?

TARGET OR GOAL – MAKE THEM 'SILVER' TARGETS

- What do you want instead?
- Which job ideas appeal to you?
- Which of your skills would you like to use more often?
- What would you love to get paid for doing?
- What do you do, even though you don't get paid?

ACTION – POSSIBLE AND ACTUAL

List all the ideas you can think of, enlist friends or a career or life coach to help you. Research other ideas from books and websites.

Which of these are you going to do?

What simple action can you do *today* to move closer to your target?

DO IT!

When are you going to do your others? Be specific — day, time, location

Plan for success — do smaller actions successfully

Keep a journal for a week while you work through these questions then:

REVIEW YOUR RESULTS

What worked well? What ideas really excite you?

What did you enjoy doing?

What was difficult, but rewarding?

What did not work? Why was that?

Was it up to you, or others?

REWARD

Treat yourself to an appropriate reward!

Enjoy the reward and the feeling of success!

BOOKS

The Work We Were Born To Do, Nick Williams. Element, 2000.
www.nick-williams.com Brings heart and authenticity into your work.

Creating a Life Worth Living, Carol Lloyd. HarperCollins, 1997.

How to Get a Job You'll Love, John Lees. McGraw-Hill, 2008 (5th edition).
Looks at your skills and how to match that to a job.

Make Money, Be Happy, Carmel McConnell. Prentice Hall, 2004.

I Can't Believe I get Paid to Do This, Stacey Mayo. Gold Leaf, 2004.

week 6 **Your friends and family**

How much love do you have in your life? Do you have enough? How do you measure it? Write a list now of everyone you love, or who loves you. This includes your close friends, family, colleagues and partner. You will have people that you have chosen and others who may have chosen you! These people are a blessing.

However, just because they love you, they may not fully support you, or provide you with your emotional needs. Revisit the 'Needs' section of Chapter 2. The people you choose to spend time with will affect how you feel about yourself, so spend time with positive, supportive, interested people as much as possible!

I heard a comment recently that made me feel really sad – 'You never make good friends once you have left school. Your best friends are those who have known you the longest'. Really? What an example of a limiting belief!

I would strongly disagree. Your best friends are the ones who know the real you, at whatever stage you are at in life. They support, listen and love you no matter what. You can meet them at any time. They may be your oldest friend, or they may not. Most of my greatest friends currently are people whom I have met in the past few years, not those who expect me to be who I was at age 10 or 16.

Which people make you feel great about yourself? Who has supported you through tough times? Who can you rely on to make you laugh, or truly listen to you? These are your 'radiators'. Individuals who increase your self-esteem and help your life to be more fulfilling and happy. To meet more of them – be open and friendly, try new activities, stretch your boundaries and friends will come into your life at any age, or stage.

The opposite are 'drains'. They are the people who demand attention, are pessimistic or negative, criticise, bully or demean you, or make you feel bad about yourself. Some of these must be edited from your life to improve your self-esteem and confidence. If you constantly find yourself dreading meeting up with someone, or feel worse after meeting them, remove that person from your life if you can. Spend that time with people who help you to feel good about yourself.

Of course, this is easier said than done, but will be worth it. Meeting people from different areas of life and with a variety of beliefs and ideas can expand your own world considerably. This variety will challenge your thoughts and ideas by being exposed to others' opinions, skills and loves, even if you don't necessarily agree with them. The more you meet and mix with new people the easier it becomes to make friends and form close relationships with people.

Do you have a wide variety of friends, or are they from similar backgrounds, professions and geographical areas? Think how you could meet other people in social settings – evening classes, clubs, sports, dancing, social groups, adventure, travel.

Client example (Alison, 33)

Situation	I would like to meet new people outside work and family. I feel the need for a new network of friends.
Target	Make three new friends in the next two months.
Actions – possible	Go to church twice a month, set up a book group, join an evening class, go to the gym or exercise classes.
Actions – actual	I am going to set up a book group. I will go to the library for details and put up a poster. I will email or phone everyone I think might be interested.
Results	The book group of eight women was set up within eight weeks, including new contacts as well as existing friends.

A few years ago I only really knew other nurses – I worked and lived with them and spent most of my time with nurses. In 1992 I moved back to Bath and shared a flat with Caroline, who is a graphic designer. It was a brilliant time. We got on really well and are still very close years later (she does all the happynurses design work!). We both found it rewarding and interesting to share our lives with people who did very different jobs.

Since then I have developed a varied group of friends, both male and female, of various nationalities – a designer, some coaches, actors, a youth worker, full-time mothers, business owners, a vet, a 'health informatics' expert, a geophysicist, a photographer/traveller and Turkish, Irish, English and Spanish individuals. There are many others I keep in touch with, some of whom I love very much.

This has happened by:

• Travelling alone and taking holidays with a group I had not met before.

• Taking courses in drama, salsa, jive, comedy, personal development and other sociable subjects where you have to mix.

- Sharing homes with others.
- Taking the initiative and inviting people to events/lunch/coffee if I wanted to develop the friendship.
- Stopping spending time with people who only 'took' from the relationship, or drained my energy.
- Finding similar people through networking events and seminars in coaching, personal development and drama, as well as comedy and improvisation weekends.
- Building up my confidence by doing scary activities – performing, singing in a band, skydiving, fire walking, abseiling.
- Approaching people I liked the look of and starting a conversation.

This all gets easier with practice and just takes a bit of time and perseverance, until it becomes automatic, comfortable and fun!

- How could you expand your social group?
- What type of people would you love to spend time with?
- What classes would you love to have a go at, but feel nervous about?

Set a date to go, take a buddy and just get started!

STAR ACTIONS

SITUATION AND SELF-AWARENESS

Think about the friends you have at the moment.

Are they 'radiators' or 'drains'?

Do you enjoy spending time with them? Do you see them often enough?

TARGET OR GOAL – MAKE THEM 'SILVER' TARGETS

What do you want instead? Who would you like to be meeting?

Who do you know already that you would like to spend more time with?

ACTION – AVAILABLE AND ACTUAL

List all the ideas you can think of, enlist friends or a coach to help you.

Look at local/national groups for friendship and activities.

Which of these are you going to do? Make a phone call, send an email.

What simple action can you do *today* to move closer to your target?

DO IT!

When are you going to do your others? Be specific – day, time, location.

Plan for success – do small actions successfully.

Keep a journal of all your actions and ideas and look at what you have learned this week.

REFLECT ON YOUR RESULTS

What worked well? What did you enjoy?

What was difficult, but rewarding?

What did not work? Why was that? Was it up to you, or others?

What will you change this week to get what you really want? Set another goal then work towards that.

Keep a journal again, then review at the end of the second week. Keep adapting your plan and keep meeting new people.

www.spiceuk.com – for activities with others.

PARTNER

The presence, or absence, of a supportive, loving relationship can affect you in a variety of ways. It depends on many factors. Are you happy with your current situation, whether you are in a couple/family or single? What would be your ideal situation? Is your current relationship one based on mutual respect, support and love? What could you do to improve this?

Any changes have to come from you – you cannot wait for the other partner to change, although that may be what you want. If you change how you communicate or react to them in a positive way, they will react differently to you. Start with yourself!

There are plenty of resources to help you establish a satisfying adult relationship and starting to look at your current situation and what you would like to be different could be a good start. It needn't be difficult.

What would you want in your 'ideal' relationship? How can you help your current one to be more fulfilling? Is a fresh start what you really want deep down? Do you feel belittled, ignored, unhappy, bored?

Go for professional help if you feel it is needed, either as a single person, or part of a couple. Therapy, Relate counselling, books and workshops are all available to help you maximise your relationship.

www.tonyandnickivee.com

STAR ACTIONS

SITUATION AND SELF-AWARENESS

Think about the relationship you have at the moment, or would like.

Is your current or future partner a 'radiator' or 'drain'?

Do you enjoy spending time with them? Do you see them often enough?

Can you communicate freely? Do they support you? Do you still enjoy sex with them? Is it frequent/satisfying/fun enough?

Are there aspects of their behaviour that annoy you out of proportion?

TARGET OR GOAL – MAKE THEM 'SILVER' TARGETS

What do you want instead? How can you talk to them about this?

Focus on the benefits of a great relationship for you and your life.

ACTION – POSSIBLE AND ACTUAL

List all the ideas you can think of, enlist friends or a coach to help you.

Look at books for ideas, talk to your partner about actions to do together!

Which of these are you going to do?

What simple action can you do *today* to move closer to your target?

DO IT!

When are you going to do your others? Be specific – day, time, location.

Plan for success – do some small actions this week.

RESULTS

What worked well?

What did you enjoy?

What was difficult, but rewarding?

What did not work?

Why was that?

Was it up to you, or others?

BOOKS

Love Smart, Dr Phil McGraw. Simon and Schuster, 2006.

Would Like To Meet, Tracey Cox, Jay Hunt, Jeremy Milnes. BBC Books, 2003.

Hot Relationships, Tracey Cox. Bantam, 2000.
How to find and keep a great partner relationship.

THE INTERNET

www.match.com

www.datingdirect.com

www.speeddater.com

www.thesinglesgym.com

CHILDREN

Welcome, parents! You have done extremely well to read this far into the book, with all your other responsibilities, or you have opened the book straight away to see if there is a miracle solution to your stresses. I am afraid I have no magical answers – but the good news is that you have some answers already and can discover many others.

As a children's nurse, I see parents coping with all sorts of stressful circumstances with some very sick children. The good news is that most parents cope well under these conditions, especially with the help and support of skilled nurses. There is some additional help available, but if you are coping with children with behavioural or physical disabilities, life can be very tough.

The parent coach Lorraine Thomas has developed different 'wheels' to use with her parent clients. In her book, *The 7-Day Parent Coach*, her 'wheel' sections are:

- home
- confidence
- relationship with children
- organisation
- health
- me
- significant relationship
- quality of life.

This is an excellent book for parents who feel their life is out of control. The chapters are very straightforward and identify that the most important step is the parents knowing what they want. Precisely. Set specific goals and keep establishing good habits for your family. One of the main factors that helped all the families was cutting down on TV, especially in the mornings when the school preparation was taking place. Be bold and ban it if that would make life easier! Habits can be changed for the benefit if all. Ask for help. Give rewards.

As in the other chapters, small actions can start to make life feel more manageable. Taking control and anticipating life becoming easier as some of these are tackled is the first step. Get help if needed, ask your partner and children to help. Too many mums can become martyrs where they feel they have to do everything around the home, or for child care. If you are harassed, stressed and tired – look at ways to reduce your workload. How much cooking/cleaning/ironing/organised activity is really important? 'Chill out' time can be good for you all!

You can make changes!

Take small steps and keep going!

Client example

....

Joanna has two small children and recounted an incident where her anger had reached crisis point. She felt she had 'done well' not to physically injure her children, but was ashamed at her lack of control and was looking at ways to prevent her feelings escalating. Psychological aggression can be just as harmful for small children. I encouraged her to put herself in her child's position. This helped her to think about what he might have wanted at the time and how that differed from what she wanted him to do. She felt that she had not taken into consideration how he might have been feeling and what he wanted.

Talking about their imminent summer holiday, we discussed what she wanted from it. She 'just wants her kids to be happy'. We looked at how that could have applied to the previous incident. If her priority had been for her children to be happy and safe, it would have led to a different outcome.

Put yourself in your children's place. What would they want? How do they feel? Have you asked them? I am not advocating giving in to them, but understanding your children and putting yourself in their place can be an important first step.

We also looked at ways for Joanna to communicate with her children without having to raise her voice louder and louder and lose control. They were to look the child in the eye, get down to their level and keep her voice calm and controlled. She also realised through discussion that praise and reward worked better than discipline and shouting. These ideas worked really well for her. Within a week she felt more in control of her emotions and her children were responding to her in a more loving way, gaining lots of rewards and praise.

Simplify your aims – aim for your children to be 'safe and happy', or you to be 'calm and have fun together'. Keep these aims in mind at all times to focus your actions.

Further help:

www.parenttalk.com

www.parentcoaching.co.uk

If, like me, you don't have children, they can still be a part of your life if you want them to be. I work with children in a paediatric unit at a general hospital. I have five gorgeous nephews whom I see regularly. I have helped with my nephew's scout troop and see the children of my friends too. There are lots of ways to be involved in the lives of children, and other adults in addition to their parents can have a big influence on them. Books often highlight significant relationships with aunts, grandparents and so on, so go on – get involved and have play!

I recently spent two hours in a car with my brother's family singing songs from 'Joseph and the Amazing Technicolour Dreamcoat' with my nephews and spent a week on holiday with my sister's family. Seeing life through the eyes of a child can be rejuvenating for tired, cynical adults!

You parents are also entitled to a break, so enlist some help and get a night away, even if that is just swapping houses for the night so someone has all the kids and you have none. Then swap another weekend the other way round!

QUESTIONS TO STIMULATE THOUGHTS

Write down your answers, ideas, questions and inspirations
as you go through the list

CURRENT REALITY – FRIENDS AND FAMILY

- What do I like about my friends and family?
- Who is my closest friend?
- Do I have positive people in my life?
- Who makes me feel good about myself?
- Who criticises me?
- What do they criticise me about?
- Are they 'right'? What evidence is there?
- What is good about my partner?
- What would I like to be different?
- Who do I know that I would like to be closer to?
- How could I take a step towards that?
- Who shares my interests?
- Do I want any/any more children?
- What would that give me?

HOW DO YOU FEEL ABOUT YOUR 'INNER CIRCLE'?

- I love them!
- They are boring
- I need more friends
- It is difficult to meet people
- I don't have time
- My partner is 'wrong' for me, but I can't tell them
- They add to my/destroy my self-esteem
- I can't be bothered to make new friends
- I don't know how to get started
- Others will think I am weird or lonely if I approach them
- No one I know meets new people
- I enjoy spending time with my family and friends
- There are aspects I love and aspects I hate

- I don't know what I would do differently
- I feel lonely inside
- I have no real friends
- I am too shy to meet people.

MY IDEAL 'INNER CIRCLE'

- Who would I like to be friends with?
- How much social/family time can I fit into my week?
- What activities would I do to meet others?
- How often would I like to see my parents/children?
- How often would I like to see my friends or partner?
- Who do I know who is happy with their social circle?
- Whose social life would I like to have/have I been interested in?
- What events would I like to attend? Can I do them alone?
- What other benefits would having more friends/a partner have for my life?

PRACTICALITIES AND CREATIVE THINKING

- Who could I ask for help?
- Where can I get information from?
- What books/magazines/journals do I read?
- What TV programmes do I feel inspired by?
- What activities do I already do?
- Who makes me feel excited?
- What activities did I do when I was younger?
- Who could I ring up tonight to invite to a social evening?
- If I had unlimited money, what would I do with/for my family and friends?

STAR ACTIONS

SITUATION AND SELF-AWARENESS

Think about how you feel about your family and social life at the moment.

How good is your relationship with your children or friends? Would they agree?
Do they have a say? Do you respect each other?

Is your anger an issue?

When are the 'worst' times for stress in your household?

What have you discovered from the questions?

TARGET OR GOAL – MAKE THEM 'SILVER' TARGETS

What do you want instead – this week, or long term?

Action – possible – List all the ideas you can think of, enlist friends, family, a therapist or a coach to help you.

Use parent books, websites and magazines for extra ideas.

Which of these are you going to do?

What simple action can you do *today* to move closer to your target?

DO IT!

When are you going to do your others? Be specific – day, time, location.

Plan for success – do smaller actions successfully.

Consistent action is the key to lasting change.

RESULTS

What worked well?

What did you enjoy?

What was difficult, but rewarding?

What did not work?

Why was that?

Was it up to you, or others?

REWARD

Treat yourself to an appropriate reward.

Enjoy the reward and the feeling of success.

You have now looked at several aspects of your life and should be feeling energised by your action and learning. If not, slow down, have a rest or go back to something you have been avoiding. Then move on to look at your communication.

week 7 Communication and confidence

In order to achieve your goals in life, you need to be able to communicate effectively – with yourself and others – and be confident.

COMMUNICATION

How do you feel about your communication skills? Can you get your point across? Do others understand you? What difficulties do you have in making your point? Who do you have most difficulty with? Do you *really* listen to others and understand *them*?

The ability to communicate starts at the moment of birth, as anyone with a baby will tell you. Even tiny infants can make their wishes known and have different 'cries' depending on what they need. Mums can pick out their own baby's cry and often know what their baby needs as they get to know them.

The skills needed to communicate effectively develop throughout childhood, but are something we learn by example from the people around us – parents, teachers, friends, associates. We are rarely taught 'advanced communication' in school, although this is one of the most important skills for success in life. Really listening to each other and getting our meaning across clearly, can improve relationships at home and work. This can make our adult lives considerably easier and more successful.

We also communicate constantly with ourselves (who, me?). The quality of what we say to ourselves can have encouraging, or devastating effects on our confidence.

"The most important conversations you have are with yourself" ROBERT HOLDEN, SUCCESS INTELLIGENCE

My life coach training was invaluable to me, as it taught me great communication skills. I had spent 15 years as a nurse communicating on a daily basis with others, often in stressful and difficult circumstances, but in my coach training I learned simple and effective techniques to improve the quality of my communications with others.

These skills can be used in work, family, indeed *any* relationship or interaction.

Rapport – establish a close connection with others through using language, body posture and listening to the other person.

Listening – *really listen* to the other person – their words, pace, tone and hidden sub-text under the actual words. Think about how to get them to expand on what they have said, be interested. Don't interrupt, think 'now it's my turn', 'wrong!' or 'how dull'. Be engaged, use eye contact and really listen with your heart as well as your ears.

 BOOKS

Time to Think, Nancy Kline. Ward Lock, 1999.
The best book on listening I have ever read – it gives me goosebumps!

Questions – Use questions to clarify what they mean, if you are not clear. Many people think 'What did he say?' or 'I don't know what you really want me to do' but fail to ask. Ask! Use questions to get the speaker to expand on the subject. Ask them how they feel about it. Use open questions – not those that provide yes/no answers.

Parents often say their children don't tell them anything. They ask 'Did you have a good day at school?'. 'Yep'. Ask better questions!

Feedback – Give feedback on what the speaker is saying to encourage them to communicate. Avoid criticism and judgement if you want lines of communication to stay open. Ask what they want, tell them how much you enjoyed that story, or how interesting the fact was; pay compliments when you really mean it. Praise them, gently, if they have told you something personal, or if they have dealt with something difficult.

 BOOKS

Drop The Pink Elephant, Bill McFarlan. Capstone, 2003.
An easy-to-read book to improve all communication – written and spoken, at work and home.

The NLP Coach, Ian McDermott and Wendy Jago. Piatkus.
Using neurolinguistic programming (NLP) (see page 82) techniques for communication, rapport building, listening and creating better relationships – an excellent book.

CONFIDENCE

What does your inner voice say to you? Everyone has one. Is it positive, encouraging and full of hope, or negative – preventing you from moving forward in your life? All the messages you have ever received have been absorbed and many of them remain with you into adulthood. Some of these messages and labels are no longer useful.

At school there were many individuals who were responsible for treating you well or badly. Teachers usually wanted a specific answer – you were either right or wrong when you answered. The fear of making a mistake, or 'being wrong' can remain throughout adulthood. It takes time and sometimes professional help, to be confident enough to risk making 'mistakes' and to be prepared to live with the risks.

Manage your risks and find out how to *reduce* the risk of failure. The only real failure is not learning from results that were different from the one you wanted and to repeat the same actions over again. Many people who are successful now 'failed' initially and continue to do so, but carry on learning and growing. You can reduce the risks of failing, or getting unhelpful results. Gather information, ask others who have done it, make sure you have enough time, money, energy, support. A fear of failure can mean never trying anything new or different.

I have had friends who wouldn't come to dance classes because they aren't 'any good'. That is why the classes are there – to teach you how to dance! If you never go to a class, you will not improve your dancing! Everything you know how to do now, you couldn't do at one point. Think of all the skills you have learned in your life. 'Leopards don't change their spots', it is said. They do if they want it enough – set a goal and take action!

If you want a different result, you must do things differently. Too often people wait for *others* to change, whereas change has to come from *yourself* first. Waiting for the right time, or to feel confident leads to procrastination. There will always be fear, until you have done something so many times you don't need to worry any more. Avoiding issues will not make you confident. *Doing* it will.

For example I am a confident, assertive person in most circumstances. I was very shy as a child, but have learned as an adult to take risks and push my limits. Last year I did 'stand-up' comedy in a couple of clubs in London, UK. If I had waited till I was ready, I would never have done it. Having performed by singing, acting and doing improvised comedy, I felt I wanted to tackle this next! The challenge was immense. When I had done it, it was amazing. It went well, I received laughter and applause and I felt fantastic. It would only have been five awkward minutes out of my life if it hadn't gone so well.

What helped me to feel I could do it was: previous experience performing, completing a comedy course, writing the best five minutes I could, rehearsing until it felt 'natural' and letting go of the outcome. I can use these techniques for any challenge. My next one is doing speaking events and running workshops on coaching issues.

Watching the TV programme 'Faking It' showed what individuals can do. Individuals were given a few weeks to learn a completely new skill and then perform it in front of professional judges. Most rose to the challenge excellently, with appropriate support, mentorship and training. Read Ellen MacArthur's autobiography *Taking on the World*, or Jane Tomlinson, completing marathons while suffering from cancer, and change your ideas about what one woman can achieve. What would you really love to do or try? What would be the first 'baby step' in getting there?

Positive self-talk is important in achieving what you want. Affirmations can also be useful, along with visualisation, expecting the outcome to be good and planning for success. Followed by action, of course. At a Tony Robbins seminar, my sister and I walked across hot coals and it was an incredible experience. The 'peak state' we got into at the start, visualisation and preparation for the finish all made us ready – we looked at a heap of glowing charcoal and stepped across it. Just writing about it brings the feelings back. The sound of 7,000 people cheering themselves was amazing!

Client example

Debbie used to find that her stress levels were extremely high on the days when she had to get her three young children ready for bed on her own. I asked her to run through what happened in this situation now and where her stress started. She revealed that as she left work she said to herself 'Oh no, I have to get the kids fed and into bed on my own. Bloody hell – how can Steve be so selfish, going out and leaving me to cope . . .' This started a whole train of negative thoughts, increasing her levels of frustration before she had even picked the children up from school. We looked at more helpful ways of coping with this weekly occurrence. She decided on a positive phrase to say to herself and decided that each Wednesday would be 'party night' for her and her children and began to look forward to this time, with fun activities for her and the children.

Eleanor asked me to coach her as she felt unconfident at work in a senior nursing role. I asked her which situations she had felt unconfident in and she recounted an episode where a consultant had been angry and it had made her cry. She was ashamed that she had 'lost control' in front of others and subsequently she was scared to deal with the doctor involved. We explored other outcomes and how she could have handled the situation differently, as well as whether the behaviour of the consultant had been appropriate.

She kept a diary of times at work when she felt things went well and when they were more difficult for her. Within a few weeks she realised that she did actually feel confident most of the time and had built up one unfortunate scenario into an event that was out of proportion in her mind. Her written evidence on a daily basis ensured that she had a more realistic view of how confident she really was on a day to day basis.

QUESTIONS TO STIMULATE THOUGHTS

Write down your answers, ideas, questions and inspirations as you go through the list:

CURRENT REALITY – COMMUNICATION AND CONFIDENCE

- Who do I communicate with well?
- How do I get my point across effectively?
- Do I avoid communicating on some issues?
- Do I get positive feedback?
- How often do I get complimented on my skills?
- Who compliments me?
- Who criticises me?
- What do they criticise me about?
- Are they 'right'? What evidence is there?
- What listening skills do I have?
- What is the most confident I have ever felt and why?
- What is the least confident I have felt?

HOW DO YOU FEEL ABOUT YOUR COMMUNICATION WITH OTHERS?

- It's challenging
- It's boring
- I don't have time to learn how to do it
- I am an expert already!
- I can't be bothered

- I don't know how to get started
- I don't know how to say important things
- I get really nervous speaking to people I don't know
- Its what everyone does
- No one I know communicates well.

? HOW DO YOU FEEL ABOUT YOUR CURRENT CONFIDENCE LEVELS?

- I never feel confident
- I feel confident in some situations
- I need more confidence
- I wish I could get started
- I enjoy challenging myself
- I could never do …
- I hate trying new things in case I fail
- I don't know what I would do differently
- I drink alcohol to give me confidence
- I use other drugs to help me through difficult situations.

MY CONFIDENCE BOOSTERS

- Who could help to improve my confidence levels?
- When do I feel more confident then at other times?
- What conditions lead to a lack of confidence?
- What would I do if I had more confidence?
- What compliments would I receive?
- How would I look?
- How could I get more confident? Alone/with another/in a group?
- Who do I know who is confident and assertive?
- What events would I like to be able to take part in?
- What other benefits would feeling confident have for my life?

PRACTICALITIES AND CREATIVE THINKING

- Who could I ask for help?
- Where can I get information from?
- What books/magazines/journals do I read?
- What TV programmes do I feel inspired by?
- What activities could increase my confidence?
- What makes me feel excited, challenged?
- Who do I like spending time with?
- How could I communicate better with my loved ones?
- What skills could I learn? Where could I learn them?

STAR ACTIONS

SITUATION

Think about how you feel about your confidence at the moment. What are your skills? What would you like more of? Note down how confident you feel in different situations for a couple of days. Be aware of how you communicate to others.

What are the times when you feel nervous/say negative things to yourself?

How can you manage these in a different way?

TARGET OR GOAL – MAKE THEM 'SILVER' TARGETS

What do you want instead?

Believe it is possible! Confidence increases by constantly challenging yourself in small ways, building up to bigger challenges. Start to speak up for yourself and note the results.

ACTION – AVAILABLE AND ACTUAL

List all the ideas you can think of – enlist a therapist or a coach to help you and use websites, books and magazines for extra ideas

Which of these actions are you going to do?

What simple action can you do *today* to move closer to your target?

DO IT!

When are you going to do your others? Be specific – day, time, location.

REFLECTION – RESULTS AT THE END OF A WEEK

What worked well?

What did you enjoy?

What was difficult, but rewarding?

What did not work? Why was that? Was it up to you, or others?

 REWARD

Treat yourself to an appropriate reward. Maybe a great book to add further skills. Enjoy the reward and the feeling of success.

 BOOKS

You Can Be Amazing, Ursula James. Century, 2001.
A book and CD for hypnosis on creating a better life.

My life has stepped up a gear since I started this – coincidence or a real influence on my subconscious?

You Can Have What You Want, Michael Neill. Hay House, 2006.
A brilliant book using NLP to help you achieve great things. Includes lots of communication tips.

week 8 Money – the root of all evil, or good fun?

Most people in the UK work for a salary and then pay for their utilities, luxuries and savings with it, so this chapter is linked with the one on 'work'. However, there are many other ways to link work, money, investments, business and rewards.

YOUR FEELINGS ABOUT MONEY

Record your reactions and answers to these questions and comments.

 ### CURRENT REALITY

- What do I like about money?
- How healthy is my financial situation?
- Who do I talk about money with?
- Do I have friends with lots of money?
- What financial skills do I have?
- What is the best aspect of my financial position?
- Does my salary pay my bills?
- What was the best I have ever felt about money, why?
- What was the worst and why?
- Spending is what everyone does
- I don't know how to make more/invest my money
- I am in debt
- I am scared that others will find out how broke I am
- My relationship is at risk because of my spending/gambling.

 ### WHAT DOES MONEY 'MEAN' TO YOU?

- Money keeps me trapped
- Money is fun!
- I am scared of money
- I don't know where my money goes
- I use money to help others
- Money is just an energy exchange between people

- I feel guilty if I earn more than my parents/partner/friends
- If I earn lots of money, others will judge/dislike me.

 PRACTICALITIES AND CREATIVE THINKING

- Would you like to earn more?
- Would you take courses to learn about money?
- Who could you ask for help?
- Where can you get information from?
- What books/magazines/journals do you read?
- What financial TV programmes do you feel inspired by?
- What hobbies do you have that could earn you money?
- How do you have fun with money?
- What business would you set up, if there were no obstacles?
- Who do you know who is wealthy?
- Who do you know with no money?
- What ideas have you had about making more money?
- What stops you doing that?
- Who do you admire for using money well?
- Who do you dislike for using money for 'evil'?
- If you had unlimited money, what would you do with it?
- If you could earn any amount of money – how much would be 'enough'?

THE PRESENT

Start with your financial position. How are your monthly finances? Are you usually in credit each month? Do you always spend more than you earn? What is the biggest problem? You *must* look at this, especially if it is causing you stress, you are overdrawn, in debt, or addicted to gambling or spending.

If you are in a difficult financial situation, there are professionals there to help. Address this issue as soon as possible. It will not go away. It is possible to find a solution.

www.citizensadvice.org.uk

www.debtbreak.com

The best activity you can do is to look at all your statements, bills and bank accounts. Compare your income and outgoings and really find out where your money goes and whether you have enough to support your spending habits. Keeping a record of everything you spend for a week is a great way to start. If the thought of this worries you, it is even more important!

If you are spending more than you earn every month, you must address this. Debt will only get worse unless you confront it and challenge it head on.

UK – A great book to help you look at your day to day finances is *The Money Diet* by Martin Lewis (Vermillion, 2004), with accompanying website – **www.moneysavingexpert.com.** There are lots of ideas and up-to-date information to enable you to analyse your financial position, save money on everyday items and formulate a realistic budget.

Taking control is the first step.

I bought his book and saved £500 over the year on everyday bills and spending. I also got the confidence to claim for mis-selling on my endowment mortgage, along with specific information and a letter template on how to do it. Within a few weeks, after completing and submitting a few forms, I received £6,100!

I rang my 'breakdown cover' provider to cancel my membership and they gave me 30% off on the spot, then suggested ways I could pay even less. They didn't want to lose my custom. My sister has also challenged her provider to get a reduction.

One of my clients used ideas in the book to save herself £35 on the monthly cost of her utilities, without changing her lifestyle. She used suggestions in the book to ask for better deals. There are also plenty of other ideas for easy, or challenging actions to reduce your outgoings or make more money – it depends how much effort you are willing to expend. *The Money Diet* was well worth the modest cover price! What difference would £35 a month make to you?

Reduce your daily/weekly/monthly spending and debts. You need to set financial goals and take control. Start to invest for the future. To create wealth you need to do one thing only – spend less than you earn and invest the difference, benefiting from the compounding effect. The interest on your money plus the interest already gained makes for huge gains in later years of savings, investment or shares accounts.

Plan, plan, plan!

My favourite few actions you can take to reduce your outgoings and control your debt are:

- Know where your money goes. Seriously – record it all.
- Shop around for cheaper deals on everyday items and services.
- Buy up on '3 for 2', or 50% free offers. Keep your cupboards full of things you use everyday.
- Always assume there is a better deal somewhere.
- Set a weekly budget and stick to it.
- Pay for all purchases in cash for a while to 'see' the money you are spending.
- When shopping ask yourself – Do I need it? Can I afford it? Is it cheaper somewhere else? (Martin Lewis)
- Set a target to pay off debt, spend less and save or invest the difference.
- Feel the pleasure in haggling and buying items cheaper.
- Find free activities that are enjoyable and fun.
- Credit and store cards are only worth using if you pay them off in *full* every month.
- Take your own lunch to work – coffees, sweets, crisps and sandwiches can add up to £10 a day or £3000 a working year!

Client example

Catherine, 31, wanted help sorting out her debts, as it was causing her stress and draining her energy. She found it useful to have a picture of her 'dream house' to focus on when her motivation wavered.

Starting with small, manageable actions, such as collecting useful information and looking honestly at her situation, we went at her pace. With regular coaching she gained the confidence to tackle the issue and used financial professionals to help her. She stopped denying the reality of the situation and explored some of her 'beliefs' about money and was able to change her thinking. She gradually felt confident that she was in control instead of her money 'controlling her'. She still had debts to pay off, but had a plan to do so and felt less stressed by taking control of the problem.

BOOKS

Also recommended are:

Your Money or Your Life, Alvin Hall. Hodder & Stoughton, 2002.
This covers spending, saving, pensions, debt.

Mr Thrifty's – How to save money on absolutely everything, Jane Furnival.
Michael O'Mara books, 2003.
For serious savings and scrimping on everything!

Detox Your Finances. 52 Brilliant Ideas, John Middleton. The Infinite
Ideas Company Ltd, 2004.
A fun, easy to read book covering the basics.

Save Cash and Save the Planet, Andrea Smith & Nicola Baird.
HarperCollins, 2005.
Ideas to save the environment and your outgoings.

If you would like to change your basic beliefs about money, challenge
your thinking and learn about more innovative ways to earn extra money,
look at **www.happynurses.co.uk.** Complete the '*happynurses guide
to wealth*' by signing up and receive emails over a year to teach you all
about making, keeping and investing money.

In this 'information age' there are many opportunities for making money
without earning each pound, dollar or euro yourself. Passive income,
owning businesses, or investing in property or the stock market are all
techniques that can be learned. Turn off the TV, join the group, learn
about them and start to think differently about money.

For example, financial freedom is the ability to earn enough money every
month, passively, that you never need to work again. Just a dream? It can
be your future if you find out how to do it!

BOOKS

For more challenging books on creating real wealth for you
and your family:

Rich Dad, Poor Dad, Robert Kiyosaki. Warner Books, 2002.
This blew my mind the first time I read it. I had no idea …

Rich Dad, Poor Dad 2, the Cashflow Quadrant, Robert Kiyosaki.
Time Warner Paperbacks, 2002.
Expands on the first book.

Think and Grow Rich, Napoleon Hill. Vermillion, 2004.
Really challenges your ideas. How the rich get richer!

The One Minute Millionaire, Mark Victor Hansen and Robert Allen. Vermillion, 2002.
A truly innovative book about wealth creation.

STAR ACTIONS

SITUATION AND SELF-AWARENESS

Think about your financial situation at the moment.

What is good about it? What issues need to be addressed?

Go to some of the financial intelligence pages on the web and start to receive some newsletters

www.moneysavingexpert.com

www.happynurses.co.uk

www.themoneygym.com

www.liveoutloud.com

TARGET OR GOAL – MAKE THEM 'SILVER' TARGETS

What do you want from your financial future? Security? No debt? A million pounds a year income? Be bold, then look for ways to get there.

ACTION – POSSIBLE AND ACTUAL

List all the ideas you can think of, you may need financial professionals to help you. Find ones with the same values and ideas.

Use books and website for information and motivation.

What simple action can you do *today* to move closer to your target?

DO IT!

Buy a note book, look at receipts, subscribe to a financial newsletter ...

When are you going to do your others? Be specific – day, time, location.

Plan for success; do smaller actions successfully.

Keep a journal of your spending for a month and see where your money really goes. Stop pretending everything is fine, if it plainly isn't and start to take control.

REVIEW YOUR RESULTS

What worked well? What shocked you?

What did you enjoy? What scares you?

What was difficult, but rewarding?

What is really urgent in your financial life?

Was it up to you, or others?

Keep writing it down each week and as your habits improve you will see the written evidence. This will help to keep you going. Buddy up with a friend and do it together.

Do something this week and feel better through beginning to take control of your money and financial future.

Well done! You have now completed eight chapters, so onto organising your life!

week 9 # Organisation and time management

In order to complete this book and create your happylife, you will need to free up some time for reading, setting your weekly targets and carrying out your actions. The good news is that you will add in extra activities that you will enjoy! You can also cut out some of the ones you don't really like too. Let's look at how you can do it.

- *How much 'free' time do you have? Do you always feel rushed and short of time? Do you spend time doing things you really love, as well as the necessities of life?*
- *How much time do you spend at work? Doing chores? Childcare?*
- *How much on Learning? Fun? Sleep? Life planning? Helping others?*
- *Do you spend time looking for items you have mislaid?*
- *Do you waste time, because you have too little that interests you?*

Start to look at how you spend your time. Keep a record for a week of what you do each day. You *can* get more done with better organisation. When I looked at how much I got completed in a 12 hour shift at work, I knew I could do more on my 'days off', even with frequent rest and relaxation periods.

Three top tips for making better use of your time are:

- Stop watching TV
- Stop reading daily newspapers
- Give up alcohol.

These three alone could free up three hours a night or 21 a week – imagine what you could do with that time!

TV – If you are thinking 'But what would I do without my soap operas?' maybe you should take action and find out. Instead of watching TV you can meet friends, play with your children, de-clutter a cupboard, spend time with your partner talking, read an inspiring book, go to the gym or a dance class, phone friends or family, write a book, plan your future goals, learn how to invest your money … what would you do?

You will cut a lot of negativity from your life by choosing not to read the latest news about war, disaster, death, terrorism, scandals and potential threats to your security. It is not important to know about *all* the disasters in the world. This is especially true if you watch TV news just before you try to sleep. You will gain peace of mind as well as time. Read about positive things that are happening in the world to give you a balanced view.

Alcohol – if you are in the habit of drinking every night, or overdoing it regularly, then cut down or stop completely for a while. Instead of waking up feeling hungover, hungry or sick and tired, you can start the day with energy, a clear head and more patience with those around you.

'It's easier said than done' I can hear you thinking. Yes it is, but worth doing, so ask a good question:

How can I use my time better?

What are my real priorities?

Then really *think* about the answer – ask the question over and over and write everything down, no matter how odd it first appears, the nuggets of wisdom will come if you keep asking yourself.

Make your *own* life as important to you as the fictional lives or 'reality' that you watch on TV, or read about in gossip magazines.

If you spend lots of time ferrying your children around to different activities, look at how you could plan in something for *you*. They do not have ownership of <u>all</u> your time. They may rather spend relaxed time with you, just 'lazing around' too!

Perhaps you really do try to fit in more than you can physically and emotionally manage, so look at your priorities, cancel some activities, learn to say 'no' to people and plans you do not want to do and book some 'down time' as well. Some of the best ideas and plans will come to you when you are just 'being'.

PLAN YOUR TIME

To use your time better – plot out on a simple time chart what activities you currently do during the day and evening and start to think of ways that you could get the jobs done in less time. Keep a diary of what you do in an average day, to highlight where you spend your time and look out for ideas in magazines and books for how you could use your time better.

There are many tools available for 'time management' but they will only work if you like them, use them and take action! If none of them suit your needs then design your own. Have some sessions with a coach, or get a buddy who will do this with you.

Take a look at:

www.fourhourworkweek.com

www.mindtools.com

www.thelifeaudit.com – I find this one stressful owing to the clock ticking on the site page!

You may have books on time management languishing on your book case, so dust them off, take the best bits from all of them and devise a system you really like.

I use an A5 spiral bound note book for my life planning and one for each project that I have on the go. In these I write my thoughts, things I have learned and read, as well as my weekly and longer term goals and actions. I look at my plan each Sunday and work out exactly when I can get the actions done. If I go for several weeks without finishing a project it is either because I don't really want to, so I leave it, or I am resisting it so I make sure I have someone to be accountable to. A coach is great for this, or you could use a friend and be accountable to each other.

This works for me but you may need to experiment with a system for you. Keep asking:

How can I use my time better?

What are my real priorities?

Also remember that some things are out of your control and as Barbara Winter says " If you have never done something before, how do you know how long it will take?" Be flexible, but stay in control.

Lots of small actions add up, so keep going and keep revising your plan. Don't give up if you feel it is 'not working', but try something new and adapt it every week if you have to. Spend time looking at what works for you and keep going until you have a system that works effectively and that you enjoy using.

Client example – using time better

Jane, 34, was fed up, feeling that she was wasting her weekends. She and her partner Adam worked hard during the week and felt they had to relax at the weekend. However, this often meant Friday nights were spent drinking too much wine. As a result on Saturday mornings they felt tired and loafed around all afternoon. They usually went out somewhere in the evening, often drinking again, so their Sunday started in a similar way with a few chores thrown in. The weekend seemed to slip away and soon it was time for work again on Monday.

I asked her what she would like from a weekend and what would be the most different from her working week. She identified that it would be a holiday. I asked her to close her eyes and tell me what words, ideas or phrases summed up a holiday for her.

They were:

- Travel, going somewhere new.

- Visiting the coast, or water.

- Taking photos.

- Going to a museum, gallery or church, that she had never been to.

- Being out all day, feeling tired and exhilarated at the end of the day.

- Feeling like a child, having fun, larking about.

I asked her whether these were activities she could do at the weekend and she said they were. She decided that on each weekend at least one of the days would be a 'holiday extravaganza'! It sounded a lot more positive than how she spent her current weekend. Together we highlighted the importance of making plans in advance, as otherwise her weekend tended to drift.

Eight weeks on, her quality of life is now much better. She has had several days and weekends away over the summer and these changes have also motivated her to join a photography evening class and write a list of '40 things to do before I am 40'.

Once you start to look at your life differently, new ideas will rapidly follow.

Another client with a family, Karen, 40, felt that she wanted to spend more time with her family at weekends. During the coaching session she revealed that she spent a lot of her weekend cleaning the house and only doing nice things when the 'chores' had been done. We explored the reasons for this and also the feeling that life was passing her by, instead of enjoying her time with her family. Her goal was to only do the cleaning that was absolutely necessary. She would involve her family in helping her and then they would all go out somewhere together each Saturday afternoon and most Sundays.

The following session was very positive. Instead of getting up early on Saturday and cleaning alone, she went back to bed with her husband for a cuddle (!), then they did some tidying together. She left some jobs unfinished and was relaxed about this as she said she was having too much fun to worry about it! All the family members were taking it in turn to choose something they wanted to do and were working together and having fun as a family team.

You too can make plans, book tickets, involve everyone and have a 24 hour 'holiday extravaganza' every week.

If you love to do lots of projects at once, like I do, you may be a 'scanner'. So get organised and revel in completing lots of projects and goals.

 BOOKS

What Do I Do When I Want To Do Everything?, Barbara Sher. Rodale Press, 2006.

Refuse to Choose, Barbara Sher. Rodale Press, 2007.

 SITUATION AND SELF AWARENESS

Think about how much 'free' time there is in your life at the moment.

How much TV do you watch, without really enjoying it?

How could you use your time better? How could you organise your 'life maintenance jobs' into a shorter time?

How could you have a 24 hour 'holiday extravaganza' every week?

What have you discovered from these questions?

 TARGET OR GOAL – MAKE THEM 'SILVER' TARGETS

What exactly do you want? When can you fit tasks/fun/relaxation/fitness in?

How could you use your time the best?

What would you like to get done that you can't fit in at present?

What would be the benefits of being better organised. Make them vivid in your mind.

 ACTION – POSSIBLE AND ACTUAL

List all the ideas you can think of, enlist friends or a coach to help you.

Look at all your options. Spend a week becoming aware of what you do, then analyse it. Know where you really are *now*.

Which actions seem the 'best' for you to try?

Which of these are you *going* to do? Keep your activity diary every day while you alter your plans.

What one action can you do *today* to move closer to your target?

Download the 'Clearing the Overwhelm' Happy Hour audio from www.happynurses.co.uk.

DO IT!

When are you going to do your others? Be specific – day, time, location.

Plan to do small actions initially.

 REFLECTION ON YOUR RESULTS

What worked well?

What did you enjoy?

What was difficult, but rewarding?

What did not work?

Why was that?

Was it up to you, or others?

Start a new week with more information and edit your organisation plan so it suits you better. Keep a record of your achievements and difficulties, then follow the STAR system for another week.

Repeat until your organisation is excellent – keep going, as it might take some time, but will be worth it!

 BOOKS

The Four Hour Work Week, Timothy Ferriss. Crown, 2007.
Start outsourcing some of your tasks!

week 10 Challenge, fun and happiness

How and where do you get excitement and challenges? Do you do new and exciting activities regularly? When was the last time you really challenged yourself physically, emotionally or intellectually?

My idea of excitement and challenge has changed considerably over the last few years.

The phrase 'That's the scariest thing I have ever done ...' now only covers activities more frightening than: walking on hot coals, skydiving, flying to a foreign country alone, speed dating, putting on an improvisation show when I had no idea what I was going to be asked to do in the next two seconds ... oh and moving to a town where I knew no one, and launching my **happynurses** coaching business.

Confidence only comes *after* the event and challenging yourself can be a great boost. What have you always wanted to try? Salsa dancing? A balloon flight? Going to the cinema alone? Going on a blind date? A parachute jump? Joining a book group? Acting on stage? Writing a film script? Asking out that woman you saw in the bar? It could be anything. Set it as a goal and take the first step ...

Review the chapter on confidence to help you.

What about sheer, unadulterated excitement? Does this question completely baffle you and you can't remember when you last felt excited, as an adult? The great thing about taking charge of your life and making changes, is the excitement. One of my clients recently said "I haven't felt this excited for ... well, ever actually!"

In my own coaching session a couple of months ago, I said I thought I had something 'missing'. We explored some of the possibilities and discovered that it was 'exhilaration'. This feeling was missing, and had been for a while, as I had concentrated on other things in my life and business. I identified activities in my business and leisure and social time that would give me this feeling and planned some activities. I now attend a drama class and am doing regular talks to nurses, as well as looking at more travel and performing opportunities.

- *How could you have more excitement?*
- *What would make you feel as excited as a child again?*
- *What did you enjoy when you were younger?*
- *What stops you from doing it now?*

Identify one simple thing that you would find exhilarating and do it as soon as possible – today is good!

QUESTIONS TO ASK

- *How would you spend your ideal day? Where? With whom?*
- *Doing what? There is no budget – use your imagination!*
- *Do any ideas come to mind of activities you would like to try?*
- *What stops you?*

Challenges lead to 'True Happiness'

The book, *Authentic Happiness* by Martin Seligman (Nicholas Brealey, 2005), highlights the necessary ingredients for an activity to provide real happiness. This is based on years of trials of people across cultural and geographical divides. His research identified that there are 'basic' pleasures – touch, taste, smell, moving the body, seeing beauty, hearing pleasurable sounds, feeling lovely sensations. These are important in feeling momentary 'happiness' or pleasure, but do not give feelings of lasting pleasure.

The conditions needed to provide lasting pleasure/happiness are:

- The task is challenging and requires real skill
- We concentrate
- There are clear goals
- We get immediate feedback
- We have deep, effortless involvement
- There is a sense of control
- Our sense of self vanishes
- Time stops.

This would explain why coaching, nursing, drama and singing bring me happiness. Others may love to play music, read, make beautiful items, act, explore nature, climb mountains. They have all the above conditions at least part of the time.

What activities do you do where you feel challenged, involved and you lose track of time? When do you feel most 'alive'? Completing a project at work? With your children? Teaching others new skills? On a beautiful beach with a great book? Playing a musical instrument? Gardening, volunteering, abseiling, swimming?

TV programmes such as 'How to be Happy', which studied the happiness of the population of Slough, showed that there can be a significant measurable rise in how happy people are, by implementing a few simple techniques.

Their 'happiness manifesto' includes:

• exercise for half an hour three times a week

• each day, reflect on at least five things you are grateful for

• cut your TV viewing by half.

Looking at the positive things in your life can make a real difference to how you feel. Decide on a day where you will not complain, or moan at all. Make a note of everything that makes you feel happy – it can be as simple as a child laughing, beautiful flowers in the park, the sun shining, getting paid, buying a new book, a great mug of tea, or receiving a letter from a friend. Write down everything good in your life for a week. It will help you to feel more positive about your life and appreciate the little things in life that make you happy. Focus on these items and see or do them as much as you can. Play just for the sake of it. You can and should do it even as a grown-up. One of the greatest forms of play for me is 'improvisation drama'. I regularly do weekend courses to get my skills back up to scratch and to lark about on stage, laughing! In reality, it's adults playing games with a theatrical purpose!

I remember taking my grandmother shopping and she saw a little cuddly teddy that she really liked. 'I can't buy that' she said (because 84 year old women never need a teddy, I suppose). I took it to the till and paid for it and she was delighted with it. She remembered the occasion and loved the bear, for a long time afterwards. Who cares what other people think? If you are not harming them, go ahead.

You can take control. Then act. It is up to you how happy you feel. Make a decision to have more fun, then find out what that means for *you*. It will be different for everyone.

One way to increase your awareness is to add your fun activities to your notes or add a specific 'fun' section to your wheel of life. Write down each day what has been fun. Don't judge your answers, just record them. Keep a record for a couple of weeks and then see what you can identify as areas within your control.

Some of mine are – listening to exciting new music on my new iPod, talking to my girl friends, larking around with my nephews, singing, making people laugh, going to a comedy club, a funny movie, a delicious meal out with some chatty friends, reading a great book in my beautiful lounge, writing my blog, learning new things, coaching clients to a better life. Yours will be different. Allow yourself to have fun just 'because …'.

These activities do not have to be expensive. Nothing particularly expensive was mentioned in my list. Simple things are often fun. Even without children you can access a theme park, watch a silly cartoon, or cycle 'no hands' along the park!

STAR EXAMPLE

Situation	I feel bored with my life, the travel to work, my job, where I live, I never do anything exciting.
Target	To do one new activity this week that I have wanted to try.
Action – Possible	I could do salsa dancing, ceroc, join an evening class, skydive, travel in a hot air balloon, take singing lessons, learn to mountain bike.
Action – Actual	I have found a salsa class on Friday that I can just turn up to. I am going with a friend from work.
Reflection	The class was great fun and I talked to two new people. I will go again next week.

STAR ACTION

 ### SITUATION AND SELF-AWARENESS

Think about how much fun and excitement you have in your life at the moment.

What activities/experiences/people do you find fun?

What challenging activities have you always wanted to try?

 ### TARGET OR GOAL – MAKE THEM 'SILVER' TARGETS

What challenging activity would you like to try? When?

What would be your 'fun' goal? How often do you want fun/challenge?

 ### ACTION – POSSIBLE AND ACTUAL

List all the ideas you can think of that you find fun or challenging or would like to try.

Which of these are you going to do?

What simple action can you do *today* to make this happen?

DO IT!

When are you going to do the others? Be specific – day, time, location.

Plan for success – do smaller actions successfully.

 ### REFLECT ON YOUR RESULTS

What worked well?

What did you really enjoy?

What was difficult, but rewarding?

Write it all down and do what was rewarding and fun more often. Plan for fun and involve others.

Start to grow through challenging yourself and feel happier by having more fun – whatever that means for you!

11 Your inner self

PERSONAL DEVELOPMENT

Learning, maturing, self-actualisation... does this mean anything to you?

The definition of 'personal development' can be a bit varied, but what does it mean to *you*? Do you live life to your values? Have you got meaningful goals for your future? Are you living a life of learning, exploration and adventure? How have you developed as an adult human being in the past few years?

If you have retrained in your job, got married, changed your career, had a child, or lost a parent, these are all events that will have an impact on you. How have you developed by choice? Have you taken courses, learned new skills, read life-changing books, looked at what you really want from life, decided to be happier and fulfilled your own needs? – well done if you have.

This does not mean there is anything 'wrong' with how you are now. You are a wonderful, unique person. However, if you would like more freedom, love, peace, knowledge or friendship in your life, they can be yours.

In the past ten years I have learned more about myself than at any other time what I like and don't like, how much I can challenge myself before I get really scared, how much sadness I can deal with, what really makes me 'tick', what I love to do, who truly loves me. Some of the changes happened 'to me' and others I chose. They were not always a success, but following those choices, I then reviewed the results overall and I have a much better idea of what good, healthy choices are for me, and I intend to make more positive ones, the more I learn about myself.

I have worked with many clients who have developed themselves through the coaching process. With encouragement and clarity they can begin to live the lives they really want, which is not necessarily what others want them to do. You can do the same. Some of these subjects have been covered in other chapters, but constant learning about yourself and the world around you can help you to develop a greater understanding of yourself.

Go back to the 'map of you' and look at what you may have discovered from the last few chapters that you wish to add on to it.

Books are an easy way to start – they can be bought cheaply or borrowed from friends or the library and you may find that they can alter the way you think about yourself and your life. Put down the newspaper and read *The Road Less Travelled*, or *Feel the Fear and Do It Anyway*, learn about new career ideas with *The Work We Were Born To Do*, or be inspired and moved by *The Alchemist*, **or** *The Monk Who Sold his Ferrari*.

All these books could open your mind to new ways of thinking and revolutionise how you live your life.

You can take the 'road less travelled' when you decide not to settle for the same boring life of TV, pub and work that lots of people think is an acceptable way to spend their limited time on this earth. You can decide to do things differently. You only get to do this journey once, or I believe so anyway, so make it count.

What dreams do you have that will not leave you alone? How can you start to explore them? How can you experience greater success and contentment, or excitement? Where would you love to be in five years? With whom? Doing what?

In the world of emotional intelligence, there are aspects of human behaviour that indicate whether a person is likely to be successful in life. These can have a greater effect than how intelligent (IQ) that person is. How is your EQ? Are you assertive, empathic and self-aware? Can you control your emotions, create rapport easily with new people and empathise with those in need? These skills can come easily and naturally to some individuals, but can also be learned.

Neurolinguistic programming (NLP) can help you to change your responses to certain stimuli, or individuals, that cause you to react in a certain way. Courses and workshops are a great way to learn about new ideas and subjects. A quick Internet search will reveal plenty to choose from.

BOOKS

The EQ Edge, Steven Stein and Howard Book. Jossey-Bass, 2006.
An excellent introduction to the world of EQ and contains exercises to help you to understand and alter your behaviour.

How To Get From Where You Are to Where You Want to Be, Jack Canfield. Harper Element, 2007.
An easy to read overview of creating a great life.

How to be Inspired, Nick Williams, Sogna Bella. Tree of Life Publishing, 2005.

Feel The Fear and Do It Anyway, Susan Jeffers. Vermillion, 2007.
A classic that got me started on the road out of rutsville!

The Road Less Travelled, M Scott Peck. Arrowbooks Ltd, 1990.

The Alchemist, Paolo Coelho. Harper, 2006.

The Monk Who Sold His Ferrari, author. Robert S Sharma. Element, 2004.

Commit to reading some of these books. Allow yourself to be inspired, challenged and changed by them.

Some of these books have similar content. Human behaviour has been studied in depth and now the answers to how you can have better health, greater happiness and more love or money are in these books. Choose one you like the look and feel of. Do some exercises and note your results. Aren't you fascinating?!

Look up 'personal development' on the internet and see how many references there are.

One of the best websites is **www.stevepavlina.com.** It is full of free information and articles.

SPIRITUAL DEVELOPMENT

When I started my personal development journey I did not know what 'spiritual' meant for me. I was not religious, despite a childhood with monthly church visits and confirmation at the age of 16. I had no idea where to start. In fact, the section of my 'life file' for 'spirituality' was left empty and I avoided even thinking about it for around two years!

As I moved forward in other areas of my life, this topic began to make more sense. My first goal was just to consider what this meant for me. I became aware of people who were deeply spiritual people – some followed traditional or alternative faiths and others were spiritual in a more personal way. Recently one of my mentors, Nick Williams said that inspiration or spirituality is doing whatever feeds your 'spirit'. This is great – for me it can include comedy, singing, nursing, teaching and inspiring others, laughing, coaching and writing and has nothing to do with being in church, which doesn't do it for me, but may for you.

You will know when you feel it.

Discover what you do that feeds *your* spirit and do it as much as you can.

QUESTIONS TO STIMULATE THOUGHTS

Write down your answers, ideas, questions and inspirations as you go through the list:

 ### CURRENT REALITY – SPIRITUAL AND PERSONAL DEVELOPMENT

- What do I like about myself?
- How do I feel when I think about myself?
- What have I learned about myself from this book?
- What would I like to learn more about?
- Do I avoid thinking about myself?
- Do I feel positive about my life?
- Who makes me feel inadequate?
- Who criticises me?
- Are they 'right'? What evidence is there?
- What was the best I ever felt about myself, why?
- What was the worst and why?

 ### HOW DO YOU FEEL ABOUT DEVELOPING YOURSELF?

- I love it!
- It's too much like school
- It sounds weird.
- It costs too much money
- I don't have time
- Why would I want to?
- It's fun!
- I can't be bothered, it's too hard
- I don't know where to start
- No one I know is interested in developing themselves.

? **HOW DO YOU FEEL ABOUT YOUR CURRENT SPIRITUALITY?**

- What?!
- I think too much
- I need a change
- I wish I could get started
- I am a deeply spiritual person
- I have habits that support and sustain my spiritual self
- I don't understand what spirituality is
- I don't know what I would do differently
- I avoid thinking about it because of bad experiences
- My partner doesn't support me
- I've tries things but they never felt 'right'
- I hate myself for failing.

 THE IMPORTANCE OF LEARNING IN MY LIFE

- How much learning time could I fit into my week?
- What would I learn about?
- How often would I meet others?
- What ideas do I have?
- How would I like to feel about myself?
- How would I like to start to develop my sense of self?
- Would I do it alone, or in a group?
- Who do I know who is happy with themselves?
- What have I learned as an adult that I use daily?
- What skills would I love to have?
- Whose life would I like to have/have I been interested in?
- What events would I like to be able to take part in?
- What other benefits would being more aware have for my life?

PRACTICALITIES AND CREATIVE THINKING

- Who could I ask for help?
- Where can I get information from?
- What books/magazines/journals do I read?
- What TV programmes do I feel inspired by?
- What spiritual activities do I do, or would I like to try?
- Would I rather be alone? Where?
- What spiritual activities have you enjoyed as a child/young adult?
- Who do I admire? Why?
- What activities do I do that support my sense of self?

If I had unlimited money, what would I do to improve my personal and spiritual development?

STAR ACTION

 SITUATION AND SELF-AWARENESS

Think about how much spiritual and/or development activity you have in your life at the moment.

What activities/experiences/people do you find inspiring?

What spiritual or personal development ideas appeal to you?

 TARGET OR GOAL – MAKE THEM 'SILVER' TARGETS

What development goal do you want to have?

Initially mine was to explore the options – meditation, reading books, being open to ideas. Yours could be more specific, or based on organised religion, or using music, reading, seminars, healing or travel to explore your options for inspiration and spiritual fulfilment.

 ACTION – POSSIBLE AND ACTUAL

List all the ideas you can think of that you would like to try.

Which of these are you going to do? What simple action can you do *today* to make this happen?

DO IT!

When are you going to do the others? Be specific – day, time, location.

Plan for success – do smaller actions successfully.

REFLECT ON YOUR RESULTS

What worked well?

What did you really enjoy?

What was difficult, but rewarding?

Write it all down and do what was rewarding and fun more often.

What inspired you?

What did you feel was a good 'fit' for you?

What can't you wait to do again?

Increase the feeling of inspiration and spirituality in your day and start to grow through looking for ideas and people to help you on your journey. Keep looking and exploring.

We have now covered all the areas of your life, so will review how far you have come and where to go from here!

Have a big reward if you have done all the exercises and if not, go back to the beginning!

12 The 12-week plan

Congratulations on reaching the end of this book! This page has several plans you can use to set your SILVER goals for each week and continue the work you have done up to now. Set aside a specific time each week to do it and take action. Keep going, and let me know how you get on!

Draw your wheel of life at the top of the page. Decide on your 12-week targets or goals for each area, or focus on one big goal for the 12 weeks.

YOUR GOALS/TARGETS

Remember to make them:

Specific	Set measurable goals, know exactly what you want
In time	When do you want it? Set a date
Life affirming	Make sure they will make your life better, in several areas if possible
Values based	They should be congruent with your values
Ethical	They should harm no one and be legal and morally right
Robust	They must be challenging, but realistic

For each topic:

Use the STAR system

SITUATION

How are things in this area currently?

What is good? What are you unhappy with?

TARGET

What exactly do you want instead? Are your goals SILVER?

ACTIONS

What actions would move you closer to your goal? Which could you do this week?

When exactly will you do them? Write your action plan.

REVIEW RESULTS

At the end of the week. Did you complete your action plan? Were the results what you wanted?

If not, what could you do differently?

WEEK 1 TOPIC	
★ SITUATION	
★ TARGET	
★ ACTIONS **When will you do them?** **Put them in your diary/notebook**	
★ REVIEW RESULTS	

WEEK 2 TOPIC	
★ SITUATION	
★ TARGET	
★ ACTIONS **When will you do them?** **Put them in your diary/notebook**	
★ REVIEW RESULTS	

WEEK 3 TOPIC	
★ SITUATION	
★ TARGET	
★ ACTIONS *When will you do them?* *Put them in your diary/notebook*	
★ REVIEW RESULTS	

etc...

Keep going! Reward yourself for taking action!
Let me know your successes!

I wish you all the best with your happier life and can be contacted for support or help at claire@happynurses.co.uk

happynurses happiness tips

For your free happiness tips and to become part of the happynurses community, sign up at www.happynurses.co.uk

happynurses seminars

Happynurses also runs regular fun and innovative seminars for nurses, focusing on coaching, happiness, life balance and communication skills as well as training its own happynurses' coaches.

For more details visit the website or send an email to claire@happynurses.co.uk